the solar system

THE PRENTICE-HALL FOUNDATIONS OF EARTH SCIENCE SERIES

A. Lee McAlester, Editor

STRUCTURE OF THE EARTH
   S. P. Clark, Jr.

EARTH MATERIALS
   W. G. Ernst

THE SURFACE OF THE EARTH
   A. L. Bloom

EARTH RESOURCES, 2nd ed.
   B. J. Skinner

GEOLOGIC TIME, 2nd ed.
   D. L. Eicher

ANCIENT ENVIRONMENTS
   L. F. Laporte

THE HISTORY OF THE EARTH'S CRUST*
   A. L. McAlester and D. L. Eicher

THE HISTORY OF LIFE, 2nd ed.
   A. L. McAlester

OCEANS, 2nd ed.
   K. K. Turekian

MAN AND THE OCEAN
   B. J. Skinner and K. K. Turekian

ATMOSPHERES
   R. M. Goody and J. C. G. Walker

WEATHER
   L. J. Battan

THE SOLAR SYSTEM
   J. A. Wood

*In preparation

the solar system

JOHN A. WOOD

Harvard-Smithsonian Center For Astrophysics

PRENTICE-HALL, INC., *Englewood Cliffs, New Jersey 07632*

Library of Congress Cataloging in Publication Data

WOOD, JOHN A (date)
The solar system.

(The Prentice-Hall foundations of earth science series)
Bibliography: p. 189
Includes index.
1. Solar system.   I. Title.
QB501.W66   533.2   78-8923
ISBN 0-13-822007-7
ISBN 0-13-822015-8 pbk.

10   9   8   7   6   5   4   3   2   1

Printed in the United States of America

PRENTICE-HALL INTERNATIONAL, INC., *London*
PRENTICE-HALL OF AUSTRALIA PTY. LIMITED, *Sydney*
PRENTICE-HALL OF CANADA, LTD., *Toronto*
PRENTICE-HALL OF INDIA PRIVATE LIMITED, *New Delhi*
PRENTICE-HALL OF JAPAN, INC., *Tokyo*
PRENTICE-HALL OF SOUTHEAST ASIA PTE. LTD., *Singapore*
WHITEHALL BOOKS LIMITED, *Wellington, New Zealand*

acknowledgments

It is not easy to be an expert in such a broad range of topics as this book attempts to address. Certainly it was impossible for the author: to the extent that I have summarized a diversity of subjects successfully, it is because my friends and colleagues in these various areas were kind enough to read sections of the book and try to tell me where I was confused. I am sincerely grateful to them: Edward Anders, Geoffrey Briggs, Alistair Cameron, Clark Chapman, Steven Croft, Fraser Fanale, George Field, Owen Gingerich, Ray Hawke, James Head, William Kaula, William Noyes, Sean Solomon, Jeffrey Warner, Fred Whipple, and Charles Whitney. (These names alone are worth the price of the book.)

I also wish to thank those who helped me assemble the illustrations in this book, especially Geoffrey Briggs, Raymond Davis, P. V. Florensky, Donald Gault, Richard Goldstein, Hartmut Holweger, Stephen Larson, Martha Liller, David Roddy, Grenville Turner, Joseph Veverka, and Alex Woronow.

contents

four

planetary interiors and atmospheres 66

five

rocks from space: meteorites and lunar samples 95

six

the sun and stars 127

seven

origin of the planets 157

one

introduction to the solar system

A good way to begin this book would be to pretend to stand off at a distance, hands on hips, and survey our solar system. Unfortunately the scale of the system and the objects in it do not permit this. If one stands far enough away to take in the whole solar system, the planets disappear because of their smallness and distance; if one stays close enough to see some of the planets, the form and scale of the system are lost. It is not even practical to draw a single map of the whole solar system to scale, because of the wide range of dimensions of planetary orbits (Fig. 1-1).

From the distance of a neighboring star, using the observational techniques currently available on Earth, nothing could be seen of our solar system except the sun. This would appear as a small, yellowish star of a type that is extremely commonplace in the galaxy. Our planetary system could not be detected. (By the same token, we are not able to confirm which of the other stars in our immediate neighborhood, if any, have planetary systems. It has seemed appropriately humble in recent decades to assume that there is nothing whatsoever extraordinary about our star and its circumstances; therefore, planetary systems are probably rather abundant in the galaxy, and life may have arisen on favorably located planets circling countless other stars. Most recently, however, as discussed in Chapter 7, this has begun to appear doubtful. It seems likely that the solar system *does* have some special properties, and relatively few other stars may have planetary systems.)

The solar system consists of very little else than the sun, in fact. This ball of incandescent gases, mostly hydrogen and helium, comprises 99.87 percent of the mass of the solar system. Most of the remaining 0.13 percent resides in a

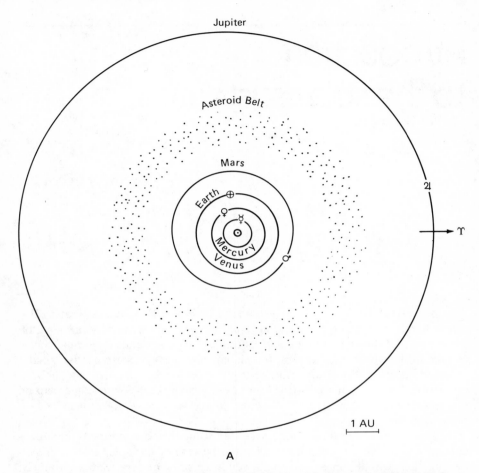

FIG. 1-1 Map of the solar system, to two scales. (A) Orbits of Jupiter and the (terrestrial) planets interior to it, and position of the asteroid belt. (B) Orbits of Jupiter and the (Jovian) planets exterior

single object, the planet Jupiter, again a ball of hydrogen and helium, in some ways similar to the sun, but much smaller, cooler, and nonluminous. If one could model the solar system so that the sun was the size of a basketball, Jupiter would be somewhat smaller than a golf ball, and would be located 500 feet away from the basketball. Analogies of this sort have been overworked, but they seem to be the only way of conveying the great range of dimensions in the solar system.

The gravitational coupling between the sun and Jupiter causes the latter to move along a near-circular path or orbit around the sun. Jupiter's motion would appear very slow in the model mentioned above, only about a third of an inch per hour.

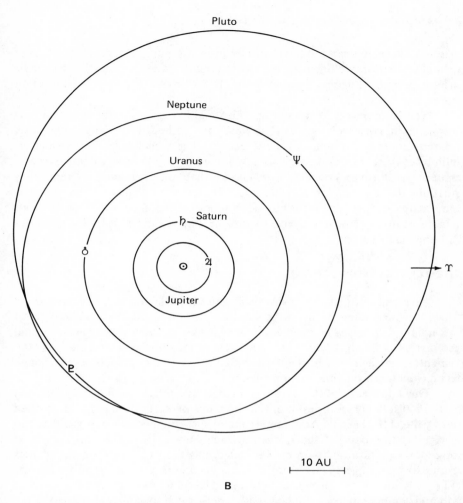

to it. ♈ is the direction of the vernal equinox, a reference axis in our galaxy. The astronomical symbol for each planet is entered at the perihelion of its orbit.

The other members of the solar system can be summarized briefly, as befits their negligible mass compared with the sun and Jupiter. There are (1) three more *Jovian planets*, similar to Jupiter but smaller, composed largely of hydrogen, helium, and other light elements, that follow orbits outside of Jupiter's; (2) four even smaller *terrestrial planets*, composed chiefly of rock materials, that move inside of Jupiter's orbit; (3) one small planet (Pluto) of unknown character, which orbits at the outer limit of the planetary system; (4) countless tiny asteroids; (5) several dozen satellites of planets; and (6) comets.

The motions of the planets and asteroids about the sun are remarkably regular. Almost all move in nearly circular orbits that lie in planes very nearly coincident with the plane of Jupiter's orbit, and all the visible planets and asteroids have the same direction of motion around the sun. Their rates of orbital revolution are unequal; the closer a planet is to the sun, the shorter its orbital period. Mercury circles the sun 1,180 times for every one time that Pluto does.

The several satellite systems are also highly organized, for the most part forming miniature "solar systems" in which one of the Jovian planets substitutes for the sun and its satellites for the planets. The comets are another matter: billions of these tiny balls of ice are distributed through a vast volume of space, thousands of times greater in dimension than our planetary system; they surround the sun and planets on all sides like a cloud of gnats. For the most part they maintain their distance, but from time to time a comet drops from its remote position toward the sun, swoops around it, and recedes again to unfathomable distances.

THE TERRESTRIAL PLANETS

As Earth scientists, our principal interest is in the terrestrial planets, those four innermost companions of the sun that are composed of the same types of minerals and governed by most of the same laws of petrology, geochemistry, and geophysics as Earth. Because the same can be said of Earth's moon, it is convenient to include this fifth object with the terrestrial planets, even though technically it is a satellite, not a planet.

Our knowledge of the terrestrial planets has grown dramatically since the early 1960's, largely as a result of the programs of scientific exploration carried out by the U.S. National Aeronautics and Space Administration. It is difficult to exaggerate the scope of the new knowledge gained, or to fully appreciate its long-term significance. Its immediate effect has been to transform the planets from astronomical objects—fuzzy images dancing in the ocular of a telescope (Fig. 1-2)—to geologic provinces, where, if it is still not possible for us to walk at will and sample outcrops, we can send sophisticated machines that analyze the soil, listen for seismic activity, and map the details of the landscape (Fig. 1-3). The opportunity to exploit these new techniques and integrate the terrestrial planets into the science of geology will fall to the generation of Earth scientists currently being educated.

The terrestrial planets fall into three classes, as a result of differences in their sizes (Fig. 1-4).

1. The smallest planets, Mercury and the moon, are airless bodies, having lost any atmospheres they may once have possessed. Gravitational attraction acts to hold an atmosphere around a planet, but other processes tend to strip it away, such as thermal escape of the gas molecules and the erosive effects of the solar wind (Chapter 4). Gravity lost this competition in the case of Mercury and the moon because of the small size and feeble gravitational acceleration of these bodies.

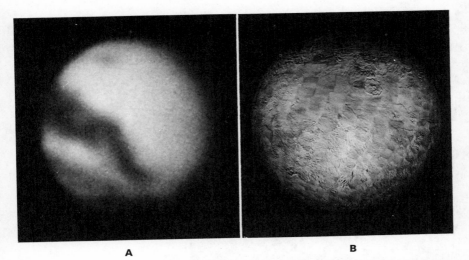

A

B

FIG. 1-2 Mars before and after the space age. (A) Photograph of Mars made by one of the best ground-based telescopes. Lick Observatory photograph. (B) Mosaic of photographs made in 1972 by the Mariner 9 mission, which came to within 2,000 km of the planet. NASA photograph.

FIG. 1-3 (Above) Landscape of rock fragments and sand dunes on the surface of Mars, photographed by Viking 1 (1976).

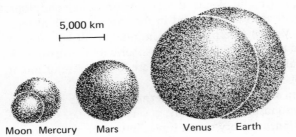

5,000 km

Moon Mercury   Mars   Venus   Earth

FIG. 1-4 (Left) Sizes of the terrestrial planets compared.

5

FIG. 1-5 Heavily cratered highland terrain on the farside of the moon, photographed by the Lunar Orbiter II spacecraft in 1966. Relatively young, dark volcanic rock (mare basalt) has flowed into the crater Jules Verne and Mare Ingenii (left and right arrows), but most of the farside surface consists of ancient, light-colored crustal rock. NASA photograph.

Internal geologic activity is related to the interior temperature of a planet, and this too is sensitive to the planet's size. Objects as small as Mercury and the moon tend to cool down rapidly, and internally driven geologic activity has effectively ceased early in their history (this observation is based largely on our knowledge of the moon from studies of samples collected by the Apollo astronauts).

Impact craters caused by the bombardment of meteorites over most of geologic history have come to dominate the surface morphologies of Mercury and the moon (Fig. 1-5), since there are no atmospheres to erode the craters or continuing geologic activity (such as lava eruptions) to bury or otherwise destroy them.

2. The largest planets, Earth and Venus, display the opposite conditions. They have retained substantial atmospheres, and in the case of Earth at least (we know very little about Venus) internal heat continues to drive complex geologic processes. Geologic activity, including atmospheric and hydrospheric erosion, eliminate impact craters in a short time so these features are of minor importance on the surface of Earth.

3. Mars, intermediate in size, is also nicely intermediate in the properties discussed above. It has an atmosphere, but only a very thin one. Geologic activity appears to have continued to very recent times, but never as vigorously as the activity that shapes the earth (specifically, Mars displays no evidence of

plate tectonics or mountain building). Consequently, Mars displays the effects of internal geologic activity and impact cratering in approximately equal abundance (Fig. 3-16).

The plan of this book is not to treat the planets one by one, but to examine various properties and processes that the planets have in common. This *comparative planetology* approach is becoming increasingly common as our knowledge of planets as geologic objects increases. The next chapter will discuss motions of the planets, Chapter 3 considers their surface features, and Chapter 4 the interiors and atmospheres of planets. The remainder of the book is concerned with the fascinating but conjectural questions of the origin and early evolution of the planets.

Chapter 5 briefly discusses the properties of meteorites and lunar samples. Meteorites are specimens of planetary material that have survived from the very beginning, the time when the planets were being put together; lunar samples, which are only slightly younger, witnessed the earliest stages of geologic evolution of a small planet. These rocks contain information crucial to an understanding of the beginning of geologic history, and we are fortunate enough to be able to bring them into our laboratories and study them in painstaking detail.

It is widely understood that the planets were formed as a by-product of the creation of the sun (a star), so Chapter 6 discusses star formation. It also asks where the particular atoms that comprise our solar system came from, and why the various chemical elements are present in the relative abundances that exist. Finally, Chapter 7 asks what there was about the formation of our particular star that might have spawned planets as a by-product. Several currently advocated models of planet formation are discussed.

ABOUT MODELS

I wonder who was the very first geologist to get it into
his noddle
That an educated guess about something would sound better
if he called it a model?
When I was a lad, models were of trains and ships,
But that was before the new generation with geology had
come to grips.
Now they give us models of everything from the origin of
dolomite to why the mid-ocean ridges are faulted,
And somehow the whole operation seems very serious and
exalted.
I believe the word model so bewitches
Because it's a dignified term for a more or less ragged cluster
of cerebral itches . . .*

---

*From R. L. Bates, "Petulant Questions," *Geotimes*, v. *22*, no. 6 (June 1977), 46.

The word "model" occurs a number of times in this book. It is v/orth discussing the source and use of the term in planetary sciences, since it sheds light on methods and attitudes that underlie present-day research in the field.

The word "model" first came into extensive use in scientific discussions when large, high-speed electronic computers became a major research tool, about 1960. These made possible a new approach to many problems. Formerly, whenever a complex problem (such as the constitution, thermal history, or seismic motions of a planet) needed to be studied quantitatively, it was necessary to express the problem in mathematical equations (typically partial differential equations), and then solve them. Not all equations can be solved formally: to cast an equation in a form amenable to solution generally requires that the natural system it describes be greatly simplified and approximated. The answers obtained by this method are not always very enlightening.

Computers made possible a different approach. These infinitely patient and hardworking machines are able to solve a complex problem by the numerical method, which amounts to breaking the situation studied into tiny pieces, then adding, moving around, or otherwise manipulating the pieces a huge number of times.

As an example of this procedure, let us consider a study of the temperature history of the interior of a planet. Each box in the grid shown in Fig. 1-6 represents a memory location in a computer. This array of memory locations has been made to represent temperatures in a planet at various depths and times. Each column in the array expresses the temperature profile at a particular time; each row expresses the progression of temperature with time, at a particular depth. In the example shown, the first row in the array represents temperatures at the surface of the planet; the second row represents temperatures at a depth of 100 kilometers (km) in the planet; and each subsequent row represents temperatures at a level 100 km deeper than the last. The lowermost row represents the center of the planet.

The first column represents temperature throughout the planet at the beginning of the time period through which thermal history is to be investigated; this may be the time when the planet was formed. Each subsequent column represents temperatures one million years later than the last.

At the outset the boxes in the array are empty. The study is begun by the investigator filling in the first column with the initial temperature distribution in the planet, probably using a hypothetical temperature profile that he wants to test the ultimate consequences of. He may also supply other boundary conditions: in the example shown, it was specified at the outset that the surface of the planet remains at 243.0°K (which is an average value for the temperature at the surface of the moon) at all times. Thereafter, the computer, following instructions in its program, fills in the remaining boxes. It uses the temperature profile in the first column to calculate temperatures one million years later (the second column); the second column is used to calculate the two-million-year (third) column; and so on through time until the investigator halts the repetitive process.

Time ➡

243.00	243.00	243.00	243.00	243.00	243.00	...
1403.19	1403.03	1402.88	1402.72			
1464.08	1464.08	1464.08	1464.08			
1522.32	1522.32	1522.32	1522.32			
1581.70	1581.70	1581.70	1581.70			
1472.12	1472.26	1472.40	1472.54			
1276.65	1277.17	1277.68	1278.20			
1114.22	1114.72	1115.22	1115.72			
951.69	952.29	a952.89	953.49			
781.19	781.84	b782.49	d			
685.66	686.31	c686.95				
575.84	576.46	577.07				
502.03	502.64	503.25				
448.50	449.08	449.66				
373.79	374.39	374.99				
322.62	323.21	323.80				
285.47	286.07	286.68				
273.00	273.60	274.21				

Depth in planet ⬇

FIG. 1-6 An array of temperatures (degrees Kelvin) calculated and stored in a computer, as it models the temperature history of a planet. Columns represent 1,000,000-yr increments of time; rows represent 100-km increments of depth.

The procedure used to calculate new temperatures is not very difficult. Clearly, in the million years between columns 3 and 4 some heat will tend to flow from box a (hotter) to box b (cooler), tending to raise the temperature of the latter; but this will be offset by heat that flows from box b to box c (cooler yet). There are simple formulas, based on the heat conductivity of rocky material, that tell how much heat should flow from a to b and from b to c in one million years, and how much the net gain or loss of heat should raise or lower the temperature at b. The new temperature obtained is entered at d. (Note that these calculations have to be made 782,000 times to carry the study through all geologic time!)

Numerous embellishments can be added to such a program to increase the faithfulness with which it imitates nature. For example, in the case described, the investigator could acknowledge the fact that rock begins to melt if a certain temperature is exceeded. He could write his program so that, after every new temperature is calculated, it is compared with the melting temperature of rock, and if the latter is exceeded the computer does a different thing than usual. It could, for instance, assume that all the hot melted rock immediately errupts to the surface, leaving residual unmelted material at just the temperature at which rock begins to melt. The pre-computer-age (or analytical) method of calculating thermal histories mentioned earlier cannot accommodate refinements of this type.

The procedure described, wherein the flow of electrons and numbers in a computer causes temperature profiles to evolve realistically from one column of a data array to the next, *models* the actual flow of heat and evolution of real temperature profiles with time in a planet, in exactly the same sense that a small train or ship can model the properties of a real train or ship. This scientific approach is often referred to as *computer modeling*. Many of the concepts discussed in this book are the products of computer modeling.

Computer modeling has lead rather naturally to another use of the word. Suppose that the investigator mentioned above tested a series of different initial temperature distributions by entering each one in turn in the first column of his array, and then let the computer crank out the consequent thermal history of the planet. Or suppose that in a series of computer runs he tested the result of changing the assumed internal composition of the planet by readjusting the values of thermal conductivity and melting temperature to those appropriate to a series of different rock types. He would be likely to refer to each of these sets of starting conditions that he tested as a *model*, meaning that it was an attempt to imitate the real thing.

From this point it is easy to slide into a third usage of the word. The above investigator probably did not chose the initial temperature distributions or planetary compositions out of the air. Each represented an idea or a hunch that seemed to deserve further investigation. For this reason, it is not surprising that *model* has come to mean much the same as *hypothesis*: "an assumption made, especially in order to test its logical or empirical consequences." This application of the word is also made in situations quite unrelated to computer studies. It might seem more reasonable simply to say "hypothesis," but for some reason this has come to be considered a pretentious and intimidating word, and is seldom used. One needs stature and confidence to Propose an Hypothesis.

Although it has become a catchword and has been stretched to mean everything from "casual idea" to "brainstorm," as Bates observes in his poem, the term "model" fills a genuine need for a word that means a tentative interpretation of a process, structure, or history that is still susceptible to extensive tinkering and rebuilding, or even to being discarded with few regrets if it is found inadequate. Solar-system science is at a youthful stage of evolution in which provocative but unproved ideas abound, and this relatively cautious term finds frequent use.

two

motions of the planets

If Earth did not pursue a nearly circular orbit, maintaining an almost constant distance from the sun, its surface temperature would vary too widely to permit the existence of such a fragile phenomenon as life. If the planets did not pursue near-circular, neatly concentric orbits, their paths would cross and they would be vulnerable to cataclysmic collisions. Quite apart from these orbit-related hazards, almost every aspect of the process by which the sun and planets were formed was affected by orbital dynamics. Clearly, the motions of the planets and the other solar-system objects are among their most important properties.

The study of the motions of objects in space in response to the gravitational forces that they exert on one another is termed *celestial mechanics*. This aspect of planetary studies is the most unfamiliar to Earth scientists, so it is appropriate at the outset of this book to discuss the nature of orbits, and present several simple formulas that are useful in reckoning planetary motions. The principles discussed are necessary background for later chapters.

CELESTIAL MECHANICS: THE ONE-BODY PROBLEM

Orbits are simplest to consider if we can make the assumption that only two bodies are attracting one another, both are rigid and spherically symmetrical, and one is vastly larger than the other (this is the so-called *one-body problem* of celestial mechanics). This is not an unreasonable approximation to make when it comes to calculating the short-term motions of one particular planet about the sun. In this situation, gravitational forces cause the smaller body to travel in an unchanging orbit about the larger; the form of the orbit is one of the conic sections (circle, ellipse, parabola, or hyperbola), and the larger body lies at the focus of the figure (or at one of the foci, in the case of an ellipse, which has two). The focus of a figure is defined in Fig. 2-1.

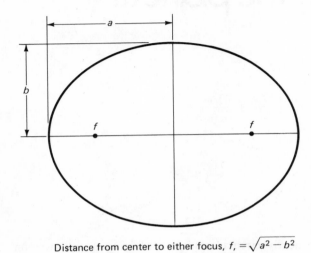

Distance from center to either focus, $f, = \sqrt{a^2 - b^2}$

FIG. 2-1 Ellipse, showing semimajor (*a*) and semiminor (*b*) axes, and positions of foci (*f*).

Description of Orbits

We need to be able to specify the size and shape of an orbit. Consider an ellipse: in geometry, this would be done by citing the dimensions of its semimajor and semiminor axes, *a* and *b* (Fig. 2-1). In astronomy, however, the practice is to use *a* as a measure of the size of the ellipse, and to employ the *eccentricity*, *e*, to describe its shape, where

$$e = \frac{\sqrt{a^2 - b^2}}{a}$$

Note that the more stretched out an ellipse, the greater is the difference between *a* and *b*, and so the greater the eccentricity. In the special case of a circle, on the other hand, *a* and *b* are identical, so the eccentricity is zero (Fig. 2-2).

The semimajor axis *a* is referred to in astronomy as the *mean distance*, because it is the mean of the closest (*q*) and the farthest (*q'*) distances achieved between two bodies as the smaller orbits about the larger (Fig. 2-3). The unit of distance used in planetary astronomy is the *astronomical unit* (AU), taken to be equal to the mean distance of the earth in its orbit about the sun: 1 AU = 1.496×10^8 km.

Not only closed orbits are described in terms of *a* and *e*, but also parabolas and hyperbolas. As we picture increasingly stretched out ellipses, *a* gets larger and larger, and *e* approaches the value 1.0. A parabola can be thought of as an infinitely stretched out ellipse ($a = \infty$, $e = 1$); an object in parabolic orbit would never reach apocenter, and so could never return for a second cycle of its

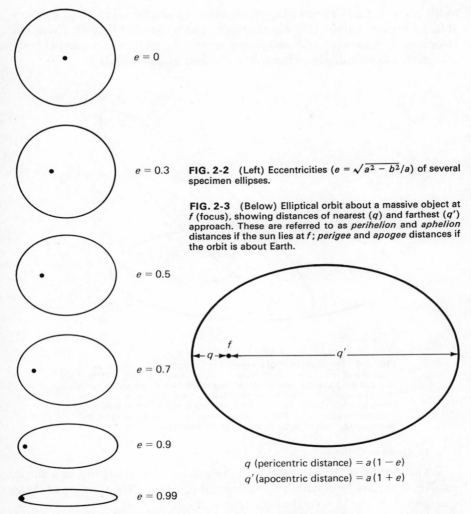

$e = 0$

$e = 0.3$

FIG. 2-2 (Left) Eccentricities ($e = \sqrt{a^2 - b^2}/a$) of several specimen ellipses.

FIG. 2-3 (Below) Elliptical orbit about a massive object at f (focus), showing distances of nearest (q) and farthest (q') approach. These are referred to as *perihelion* and *aphelion* distances if the sun lies at f; *perigee* and *apogee* distances if the orbit is about Earth.

$e = 0.5$

$e = 0.7$

$e = 0.9$

$e = 0.99$

q (pericentric distance) $= a(1 - e)$
q' (apocentric distance) $= a(1 + e)$

orbit. Definitions of a and e for hyperbolas are harder to relate to orbital shapes, as the following summary shows:

	a	e
circle	finite, positive	0
ellipse	finite, positive	$0 < e < 1$
parabola	infinite	1
hyperbola	finite, negative	> 1

More will be said later about hyperbolas.

In addition to a and e, which describe the size and shape of an orbit, several other parameters are needed to specify the *orientation* of the orbit relative to the plane of Earth's orbit (the *ecliptic* plane, by definition) and to the galaxy at large. Principal among these is the orbital inclination, *i* (Fig. 2-4). These and several other parameters that completely specify the motion of a celestial body are referred to collectively as the *orbital elements* of that object.

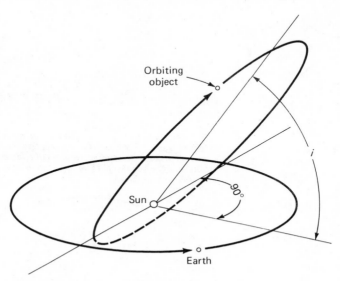

FIG. 2-4 The inclination of an orbit, *i*, is the angle between the plane it lies in and the plane of Earth's orbit (*ecliptic plane*). Orbital motion is *direct* or *prograde* (i.e., counterclockwise as we look down on the north pole of the solar system) for all planets and most other objects we are concerned with; *retrograde* (clockwise) orbits are assigned very high inclinations (90° ≤ *i* < 180°): one pretends that they are direct orbits so highly inclined as to be flipped over on their backs.

Motions in Orbit

The motion of a body subject to the gravitational attraction of a single massive object can be described by differential equations. The solution of these equations gives rise to several simple relationships.

1. The *period*, *P*, of the small body, the time it takes to complete one circuit of its orbit, is fixed by the relationship

$$P^2 = \frac{4\pi^2 a^3}{GM} \tag{2-1}$$

where *M* is the mass of the large body about which it orbits, and *G* is the universal gravitational constant (6.668×10^{-8} cm³/g sec²). Note that periods are longer, the greater the mean distance; as already noted, the planets farthest from the sun take the longest to go once around their orbits (Table 2-1). Also, for a given mean distance, the more massive a central body is the faster objects will orbit about it. If the sun were twice as massive as it is, Earth's period would be only $1/\sqrt{2}$ as long as it is; a year would pass in 258 days. Obviously, this formula only holds for closed orbits; parabolas and hyperbolas do not have "periods."

Table 2-1 Dynamical Properties of the Planets and the Three Largest Asteroids

	Mass, Relative to Earth[a]	Mean Distance a (AU)	Eccentricity e	Inclination i (degrees)	Orbital Period P (Earth years)	Mean Orbital Velocity (km/sec)	Escape Velocity from Surface of Planet (km/sec)	Rotation Period (hr)	Obliquity of Rotation Axis (degrees)[b]
MERCURY	0.055	0.387	0.206	7.0	0.241	47.9	4.3	1,406	<3
VENUS	0.816	0.723	0.007	3.39	0.615	35.0	10.4	5,832[c]	3
EARTH	1.000	1.000	0.017	0.00	1.000	29.8	11.2	24	23.5
MARS	0.108	1.524	0.093	1.85	1.881	24.1	5.0	24.5	24.0
ASTEROIDS									
VESTA	0.00004	2.361	0.088	7.1	3.63	19.4	0.34	10.6	?
CERES	0.00021	2.767	0.079	10.6	4.60	17.9	0.57	9.1	?
PALLAS	0.00003	2.767	0.235	34.8	4.61	17.9	0.31	10?	?
JUPITER	317.9	5.203	0.048	1.31	11.86	13.1	60.2	9.8	3.1
SATURN	95.2	9.54	0.056	2.49	29.46	9.6	36.2	10.3	26.7
URANUS	14.6	19.18	0.047	0.77	84.0	6.8	22.4	24[c]	82.1
NEPTUNE	17.2	30.07	0.009	1.78	164.8	5.4	23.9	22	28.8
PLUTO	0.1(?)	39.44	0.249	17.2	247.7	4.7	?	150	?

[a]Mass of Earth: 5.975×10^{27} g.
[b]Angle between rotation axis and an axis perpendicular to the plane of the planet's orbit.
[c]Retrograde rotation.

2. We need to know the radial distance r between a major body and a minor body when the latter is at various orbital positions; this remains constant only in the case of circular orbits. In the case of elliptical and hyperbolic orbits, it obeys the relationship

$$r = \frac{a(1 - e^2)}{1 + e \cos \theta} \qquad (2\text{-}2a)$$

where θ is the angular distance from the pericentric position (see Fig. 2-5). The formula does not apply to parabolic orbits, where a is infinite; q, the pericentric distance, has to be used instead of a to express the scale of a parabolic orbit. In this case, Eq. (2-2a) takes the form

$$r = \frac{2q}{1 + \cos \theta} \qquad (2\text{-}2b)$$

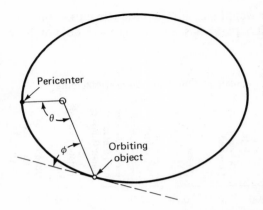

FIG. 2-5 Definition of angles θ and ϕ used in Eqs. (2-2) and (2-5).

3. The velocity, v, of an object at any point in its orbit is given by the equation

$$v^2 = 2GM\left(\frac{1}{r} - \frac{1}{2a}\right) \tag{2-3}$$

which is valid for all types of orbits.

A number of interesting consequences follow from this and the preceding formulas. First, note that for a circular orbit, r always equals a, so v equals the constant velocity $\sqrt{GM/a}$; but in other types of orbits, v varies with r. The object always moves fastest where r is smallest, that is, at pericenter. In elliptical orbits, v is of course smallest where r is greatest, at apocenter. A practical application of these velocity variations is shown in Fig. 2-6. This exercise points up the fact that an object in elliptical orbit travels faster at pericenter than it would in a circular orbit at the same distance from the attracting center, and, conversely, slower at apocenter than the circular velocity.

FIG. 2-6 The period of a circular orbit varies with a (Eq. 2-1) : a value of a can be chosen for an artificial Earth satellite such that P is just 24 hr (the rotation period of Earth), so the satellite appears to hang motionless above an observer on Earth's surface. This is a particularly advantageous situation for communications relay satellites. The value of a needed for a synchronous orbit can be determined by rearranging Eq. (2-1) and setting $P = 24$ hr:

$$a^3 = \frac{P^2 GM}{4\pi^2} = \frac{(24 \text{ hr})^2 (6.668 \times 10^{-8} \text{ cm}^3/\text{g}\cdot\text{sec}^2)(5.98 \times 10^{27} \text{ g})}{4\pi^2}$$
$$= 75.4 \times 10^{27} \text{ cm}^3$$
$$a = 4.225 \times 10^9 \text{ cm} = 42{,}250 \text{ km}$$

The velocity in synchronous orbit, 3.07 km/sec, can be determined from Eq. (2-3), or by dividing $2\pi a$ (the orbital circumference) by 24 hr.

Satellites are usually launched first into a low, circular parking orbit. For an altitude of 400 km,

$$a = 400 \text{ km} + 6371 \text{ km (Earth's radius)} = 6{,}771 \text{ km}$$

Velocity in the parking orbit, calculated from Eq. (2-3), is 7.67 km/sec.

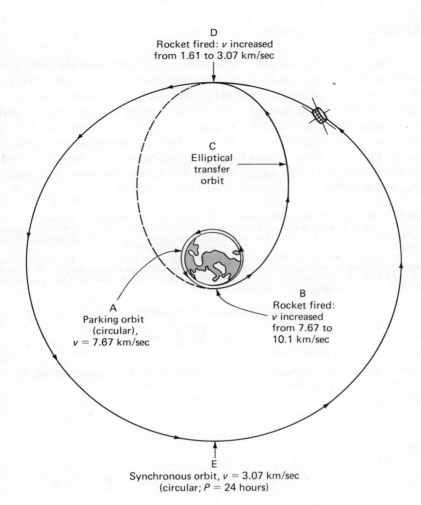

D
Rocket fired: v increased
from 1.61 to 3.07 km/sec

C
Elliptical
transfer
orbit

A
Parking orbit
(circular),
v = 7.67 km/sec

B
Rocket fired:
v increased
from 7.67 to
10.1 km/sec

E
Synchronous orbit, v = 3.07 km/sec
(circular; P = 24 hours)

How to transfer the satellite from parking orbit to synchronous orbit? This is commonly accomplished by accelerating the satellite into an elliptical orbit that extends from the former parking orbit out to the synchronous distance. The characteristics of the required elliptical orbit are easily found: $2a$ must equal $q + q'$ (Figs. 2-1 and 2-3), and we want q to be the same as the radius of the original parking orbit, while q' must equal the synchronous orbit radius: $2a$ = 6,771 km + 42,250 km. Then, from Fig. 2-3,

$$1 - e = \frac{q}{a} = \frac{6,771 \text{ km}}{24,510 \text{ km}} = 0.276$$
$$e = 1 - 0.276 = 0.724$$

Knowing a and e, we can solve Eq. (2-3) for perigee velocity ($r = q$; v then equals 10.1 km/sec) and apogee velocity ($r = q'$; v = 1.61 km/sec) in the elliptical transfer orbit. The transfer is accomplished, then, by firing a rocket engine while the spacecraft is in parking orbit until its velocity is increased from 7.67 km/sec (circular velocity) to 10.1 km/sec. Thrust is applied in the direction of motion in the parking orbit; at 10.1 km/sec, however, the spacecraft cannot remain in such a low circular orbit, but must swing out into the ellipse just calculated. At apogee the engine is fired one more time, until the velocity is increased from 1.61 to 3.07 km/sec; this is enough to remove the spacecraft from its elliptical orbit and place it in a circular (synchronous) orbit. The maneuver as a whole is referred to as a *Hohmann transfer*.

17

Second, Eq. (2-3) makes clearer to us the meaning of parabolic and hyperbolic orbits. Remember that a is infinite for parabolic orbits, so that in this case the last term in Eq. (2-3) is zero; r gets greater and greater as an object moves out from pericenter, so v^2 becomes progressively smaller. The essential property of a parabolic orbit is that an object following it approaches zero velocity as its distance from the attracting body becomes infinite. An object in hyperbolic orbit, on the other hand, would keep on traveling at some finite speed as r approached infinity. ($1/r$ in Eq. (2-3) approaches zero; but since a is negative finite, v^2 approaches some constant finite value, not zero.)

FIG. 2-7 Deflection of an asteroidal fragment from its original elliptical orbit by passage near Earth (schematic). Up to A, solar gravity dominates the fragment's motion; along BC terrestrial gravity dominates; in the intervals AB and CD both forces compete. Beyond D, a new orbit about the sun is established.

Gravitational force equals GM_1M_2/r^2 (G = gravitational constant, M_1 and M_2 are the masses of two objects attracting one another, r = distance between them); so we can calculate the distance r from Earth inside which terrestrial gravity begins to dominate. At this distance solar gravitational force equals the terrestrial gravitational force, so

$$\frac{GM_{sun}M_{fragment}}{(1\ AU)^2} = \frac{GM_{Earth}M_{fragment}}{r^2}$$

$$r^2 = \frac{M_{Earth}}{M_{sun}}(1\ AU)^2 = \frac{5.98 \times 10^{27}\ g}{1.99 \times 10^{33}\ g}(1.496 \times 10^8\ km)^2$$

$$r = 259{,}000\ km$$

which is a much smaller sphere of influence than is implied by the accompanying sketch.

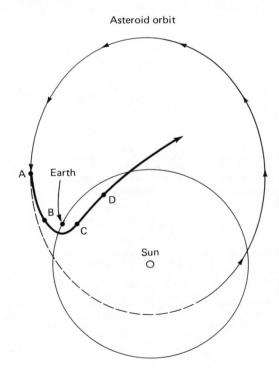

Asteroid orbit

In practical terms, we can think of near-parabolic and hyperbolic orbits for objects that, at a great distance from an attracting center, have respectively very small and not-so-small velocities relative to the attracting center. Consider an asteroidal fragment whose orbit crosses Earth's (Fig. 2-7). For many years Earth might never be near one of the crossings (*nodes*) of the orbits when the fragment came by, and the latter would pursue a normal elliptical orbit about the sun. Suppose that there was finally a close encounter. The gravitational pull of the sun would greatly outweigh Earth's up to point A, and the usual elliptical orbit would persist up to there. Between A and B both forces would be comparable, and a path not describable by the formulas of this chapter would be followed. By the time B was reached, the original situation would be reversed; Earth's gravitation would outweigh the sun's, and the object would fall into orbit around Earth. Since the fragment moved with considerable velocity (some portion of its original elliptical velocity) at A (a "great distance" from Earth), the orbit it adopted around Earth would be hyperbolic, not elliptical. If perigee distance of this orbit happened to be less than Earth's radius, the two would collide; we would have a new meteorite. Otherwise, the fragment would arc around the earth and be fired off along CD toward infinity. Only temporarily, however; by point D, solar gravity would reassert itself, and the fragment would probably enter a new orbit around the sun. Orbital changes that occur when an object is gravitationally influenced by some massive object that it passes near, other than the principal attracting center that it orbits about, are called *perturbations*.

Third, we can explore the concept of "escape velocity." For one object to escape the gravitational influence of another means that the former moves outward in such an orbit that it will never fall back toward or around the latter. As we have just seen, a parabolic or hyperbolic orbit fulfills this requirement. For a parabolic orbit $a = \infty$; so Eq. (2-3) becomes

$$v_e^2 = \frac{2GM}{r} \tag{2-4}$$

Here v_e, the parabolic or *escape* velocity, represents the least possible velocity needed to send an object away from an attracting center of mass M, never to return; a higher velocity would be required to send the object away in a hyperbolic orbit. Note that v_e is not a constant for any given attracting center; its value depends upon the distance from the attracting center. Thus an object at the surface of the sun would have to be projected at 617 km/sec to escape the sun, but at 1 AU escape velocity from the sun is only 42 km/sec. Escape velocities from the surfaces of the various planets are shown in Table 2-1.

Escape velocity works in reverse, too. If at least v_e is needed to escape from the surface of a planet or other object, then any object coming from space and colliding with this surface must do so with a velocity of at least v_e. An object that once hung nearly motionless relative to the sun, at a great distance from it, would be gravitationally attracted by the sun and would fall faster and faster toward it. At any point the falling object's velocity would equal the escape velocity, but of course its direction of motion would be the opposite of that needed to escape. If the object, instead of hanging motionless at the outset, had some appreciable component of velocity toward the sun, the object would ultimately impact the sun at (v_e + original intrinsic velocity).

One last important formula of celestial mechanics:

$$(rv \sin \phi)^2 = GMa(1 - e^2) \tag{2-5a}$$

for elliptical or hyperbolic orbits, and

$$(rv \sin \phi)^2 = 2GMq \tag{2-5b}$$

for parabolic orbits (ϕ is defined in Fig. 2-5). Used together, Eqs. (2-3) and (2-5) allow us to calculate a and e for the orbit of any object in the solar system (or other gravitating system), given only the position and velocity vector of the object at any one time. It is essentially by this means that orbital parameters have been derived for planets, satellites, comets, asteroids, etc. These two formulas are used in Fig. 2-8 to demonstrate that massive rocket boosters are not needed to launch an object into Earth orbit.

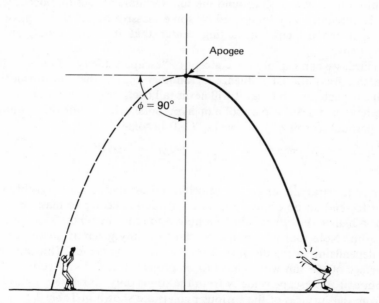

FIG. 2-8 A ball thrown or batted into the air is actually in orbit about the center of Earth! The ball has no way of knowing that the attracting center it feels is a great distended sphere with which it will soon collide. For all it knows, Earth's 5.98×10^{27} g might be concentrated at the center of the true Earth, and it attempts to perform an elliptical orbit about the center.

Violations of the One-Body Situation

Real astronomical systems always violate the simplifying assumptions underlying the one-body problem to some degree. Often the violations are so trivial that we can ignore them, but sometimes they are not; let us consider qualitatively how various kinds of violations affect the motions of orbiting bodies.

Suppose that the two bodies are comparable in size, instead of one being vastly larger than the other? In this case (the two-body problem), if we consider our vantage point or reference frame to be located at the center of one of the bodies, it would appear to us that the other body was describing an orbit having the shape of a conic section about us, just as in the one-body situation; the only difference would be that, where M (mass of the attracting center) appears in the formulas given above, $M_1 + M_2$ must now be used (the sum of the masses of both bodies). If we could view the system from a station fixed in space rather than on either of the two bodies, we would see that *both* were in motion, orbiting in conic sections about the center of mass of the pair. Thus, for example, Earth would be seen to be wobbling about a point some 4,750 km above its center (i.e., the center of mass of the Earth–moon system); similarly, the sun orbits about a

Assuming that v for the ball at apogee is 10 m/sec, we can rearrange Eq. (2-3) to find a for its would-be orbit:

$$\frac{1}{2a} = \frac{1}{r} - \frac{v^2}{2GM}$$

$v^2/2GM$ turns out to be negligibly small compared to $1/r$, however; so for all intents and purposes $a = r/2$ (half of Earth's radius) or 3,186 km. Knowing a, Eq. (2-5) can be solved for e:

$$1 - e^2 = \frac{2rv^2 \sin^2 \phi}{GM} = \frac{(2)(3{,}186 \text{ km})(10 \text{ m/sec})^2(1)^2}{(6.668 \times 10^{-8} \text{ cm}^3/\text{g}\cdot\text{sec}^2)(5.98 \times 10^{27} \text{ g})}$$

$$= 0.0000016$$
$$e^2 = 0.9999984$$
$$e = 0.9999991 \quad \text{(almost parabolic)}$$

Suppose that Earth's mass really were concentrated at its center; we could follow the ball's progress in orbit using the formulas presented above. From Eq. (2-1) we calculate an orbital period of only 566 sec; it would take the ball less than 5 min to fall from apogee to perigee on the other side of Earth's center. Perigee distance is calculated from a formula in Fig. 2-3:

$$q = a(1 - e) = (3{,}186 \text{ km})(0.0000009) = \text{only 290 cm}$$

Finally, we learn the ball's rather impressive perigee velocity from Eq. (2-3):

$$v^2 = 2GM\left(\frac{1}{r} - \frac{1}{2a}\right)$$

In this case $1/2a$ is negligible compared with $1/r$ $(= 1/q)$; so

$$v^2 = \frac{2GM}{r}$$
$$= \frac{(2)(6.668 \times 10^{-8} \text{ cm}^3/\text{gm}\cdot\text{sec})^2(5.98 \times 10^{27} \text{ g})}{290 \text{ cm}}$$
$$= 2.75 \times 10^{18} \text{ cm}^2/\text{sec}^2$$
$$v = 16{,}600 \text{ km/sec}$$

point 738,000 km from its own center, that is, the center of mass of the sun–Jupiter system.

What if the orbiting bodies are not rigid? In fact, a great many orbiting objects aren't; stars and large planets behave as fluid spheres, not solids. Only objects of asteroidal and smaller dimension can be treated as solids. The gravitational pull that a deformable object feels as it orbits about an attracting center (Fig. 2-9) tends to distort its form somewhat, drawing it out into a fluid egg shape. This "egg" wants to keep its long axis pointed toward the attracting center; but if the fluid object we have in mind is rotating (as well as orbiting), the rotation tends to carry the long axis away from this preferred orientation. The fluid body continually adjusts its shape in an effort to bring its long axis to

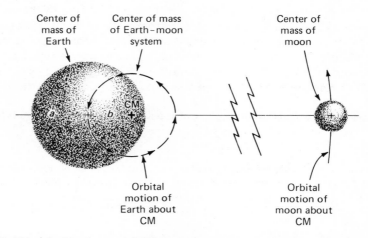

Center of mass of Earth Center of mass of Earth–moon system Center of mass of moon

Orbital motion of Earth about CM Orbital motion of moon about CM

FIG. 2-9 Tides: Earth and moon orbit about the center of mass of the Earth–moon system (CM), which is located 1,630 km deep inside Earth. The center of mass of Earth feels a centrifugal acceleration as it rotates about CM; this is exactly balanced by the gravitational pull of the moon:

$$\frac{4\pi^2 S_e}{P^2} \text{ (centrifugal acceleration)} = \frac{GM_m}{(S_e + S_m)^2} \text{ (gravitational acceleration due to moon)}$$

Here P is the orbital period about CM, S the distance to CM, and M stands for mass; the subscripts e and m denote Earth and moon. An analogous balance of forces governs the motion of the moon abour CM.

This balance of forces obtains only for the centers of mass of the two objects, however. If we consider the situation somewhere else in Earth or moon, at a point away from the center of mass but constrained to travel along with it, we find an imbalance of forces. At a in Earth, S_e is larger than the distance between CM and Earth's center of mass; this means that a experiences a greater centrifugal acceleration, but a slightly smaller lunar gravitational pull, than Earth's center of mass (see above equation). Thus there is a net acceleration or pull of the material at a away from the moon; this results in a distortion of the form of Earth, producing a bulge that points away from the moon.

Conversely, at b, the lunar gravitational acceleration exceeds the centrifugal acceleration; this opposite force imbalance produces another bulge in Earth, pointing toward the moon. Most of the distortion in Earth's form occurs in its highly mobile outer layer, the oceans. For exactly analogous reasons, the gravitational acceleration of Earth distorts the form of the moon so that it bulges toward and away from Earth.

bear on the attracting center; but readjustment takes time, so it is never completely successful. The long axis of the distorted body lags somewhat behind its desired position.

But what has this distortion to do with orbits? A planet or satellite can be (indeed always is) endowed with *spin* or angular momentum in two different categories—that associated with its orbital motion about some other attracting body, and that associated with its rotation. If the two bodies were rigid, these two angular momenta would remain completely independent of one another, and orbital motion would not be affected in the least by planetary rotations. The importance of lagging tidal deformations is that they provide a mechanism by which, over a period of time, angular momentum is shifted from one category to the other, as set forth in Fig. 2-10. If angular momentum is added to or subtracted from an orbit, the orbit must change. As a result of the torques noted in

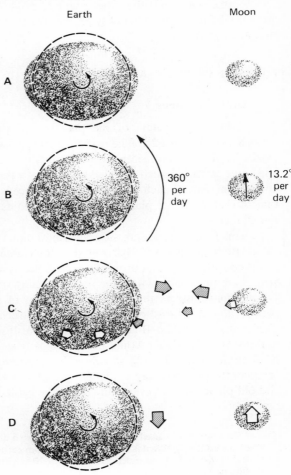

Earth   Moon

360° per day   13.2° per day

FIG. 2-10 Earth–moon relationships (viewed from the north pole; greatly exaggerated). Earth is tidally distorted by the moon into an ellipsoid (A), as noted in Fig. 2-9. The long axis of the ellipsoid does not point directly at the moon, however, because Earth's relatively rapid rotation carries it out of alignment. Earth continually flexes its form to reestablish alignment, but not promptly enough: the tidal bulge always lags in the direction of Earth's rotation; it cannot "catch up" with the Earth–moon axis (B). One bulge feels the moon's gravitational attraction more strongly than the other, being slightly nearer (C). The net effect of this imbalance of forces is to cause Earth's near-lunar bulge to be pulled moonward; that is, Earth feels a small clockwise turning force or torque (D), which over long periods of time slows its rotation. Conversely, the lunar orbital velocity is accelerated, causing an increase in the moon's mean distance from Earth.

Fig. 2-10, the mean distance of the moon from Earth is increasing at a rate of ~ 3 cm/yr*, and the rotation of Earth is slowing at such a rate that the day becomes ~ 0.0016 sec longer every century.

Suppose that there are more than two gravitating bodies? In this case orbital motion becomes very difficult to determine; simple formulas are no longer sufficient. Recall that in Fig. 2-7 the one-body approximation was good enough to describe the motion of an asteroidal fragment up to point A, and from B to C; but between A and B, where the effects of solar and terrestrial gravity are comparable, it would be necessary to solve the equations of motion numerically (see Chapter 1) in order to follow the course of the fragment.

Planets of the solar system do not approach one another closely, so each feels predominantly the pull of the sun, and the short-term behavior of planetary orbits can be well approximated by the one-body formulas. Yet each planet *is* feebly attracted by all the other planets, and over long periods of time these additional forces can effect changes (*secular perturbations*) in orbital parameters that are significant.

MOTIONS OF THE PLANETS

Orbital Motions

Orbital parameters of the planets and the three largest asteroids are summarized in Table 2-1. The regularity of the planetary system is demonstrated by the small values of eccentricity and inclination (except in the cases of Pluto and some asteroids, such as Pallas). The progression of mean distances expresses another regularity; each planet's mean distance is about 75 percent greater than that of the next inner planet. (Here the asteroids are considered collectively as one planet.)

This geometric progression of orbital dimensions (Fig. 2-11) is named the Titius–Bode law and was discovered in the eighteenth century. For many years it was considered to be a property of the solar system that was established at the very beginning, and a vital clue for unraveling the mystery of the origin of the system. Astronomers required their theories of solar system origin to spawn planets at the Titius–Bode distances. More recently, however, it has seemed likelier that the Titius–Bode law simply expresses the closest spacing of planets in the solar system that would be dynamically stable over long periods of time. If additional planets could somehow be inserted in circular orbits between the orbits of the present array of planets, gravitational interactions between the new and old planets would eventually cause the orbits of both to be modified. After

---

*The symbol $\sim$ is used extensively in this book to denote "approximately." The degree of uncertainty implied is variable, ranging from perhaps 10 percent in some cosmochemical applications to as much as a factor of 10 in either direction in some astrophysical situations.

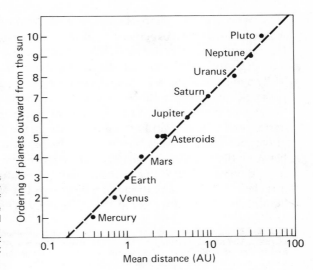

FIG. 2-11 The spacing of planets in the solar system appears fairly regular if a logarithmic scale of mean distances is used, and if the asteroids collectively are considered to be a planet. The dashed line corresponds to a spacing law such that each planet's orbit is 75 percent larger than the next inner one.

a series of orbital perturbations, occurring over a period of time, intersecting orbits would be established. Some of the planets in the overcrowded system would be eliminated by collisions and/or by close encounters similar to that of Fig. 2-7. Such near-misses can have the effect of whipping the smaller object out of the solar system altogether. Eventually, the solar system would again be reduced to a set of planets spaced far enough apart to prevent substantial gravitational interactions.

Rotations

The rotation periods of the planets (Table 2-1) display another remarkable regularity, and one that is not understood. The periods of most of the planets and many of the asteroids (i.e., objects enormously different in mass, composition, and position in the solar system) are nearly the same, the order of 10 hr. The principal known exceptions are Mercury and Venus; but, as discussed below, tidal effects have changed the rotation rates of these innermost planets from whatever they might have been earlier to their present values.

Figure 2-10 suggests how gravitational forces exert a torque on a rotating, tidally distorted body, tending to slow its rotation. A small body (the moon) is shown slowing the rotation of a larger one (Earth), but the process works the other way, too. The moon undoubtedly rotated more rapidly at one time, but its spin was reduced by torques exerted by Earth's gravity on its own tidal bulges. Eventually, it reached its present stable state, wherein it rotates just once during the circuit of its orbit so that the same side of the moon always faces the earth. Since rotation relative to the Earth–moon axis has ceased, the lunar tidal-bulge no longer lags behind the Earth–moon line; it points directly at Earth, and the pull of Earth's gravity on it does not torque the moon's rotation one way or the other.

Why did this one particular face of the moon settle down to face Earth instead of another? Irregularities of mass distribution in the moon determined the orientation. Here we refer to intrinsic irregularities, quite apart from the temporary tidal deformations discussed above. In any body that is not spherically symmetric, there is one particular axis about which the planet's mass is gathered more closely (however slightly) than any other possible axis. (This is the axis of the smallest principal moment of the inertia. In a football it would correspond to a straight line running through the pointed ends of the ball.) The gravitational acceleration between two bodies is strongest, for a given distance between their centers of mass, if their minimum axes of inertia are aligned toward one another. If one of the bodies was rotating, but at a diminishing rate, it is clear that the orientation it finally stopped at would be the one that pointed its minimum axis of inertia at the other body. This is what happened with the

FIG. 2-12 Spin–orbit coupling in Mercury, the closest planet to the sun. The minimum axis of inertia in Mercury is indicated by a line with one end tagged. At perihelion (*p*), the minimum inertia axis is aligned with the sun. As Mercury orbits one time around the sun, it rotates $1\frac{1}{2}$ times on its own axis, so that when it returns to perihelion its minimum inertial axis is again aligned with the sun, but reversed 180° from the last perihelion passage.

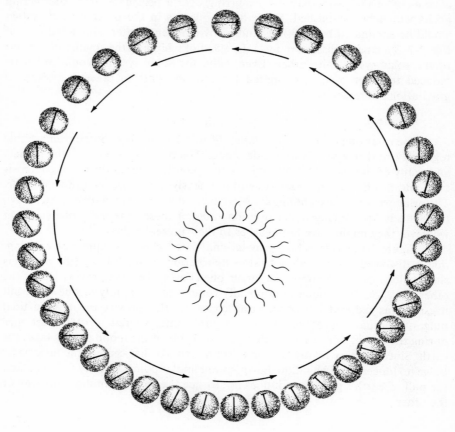

p

moon: the face we always see corresponds inertially to one pointed end of a football.

The planet Mercury, whose original rotation has been slowed by powerful tidal effects of the sun, illustrates a more complex type of spin–orbit coupling (Fig. 2-12). Mercury's orbit is more eccentric than that of most planets, and the tidal acceleration of the sun is strongest at Mercury's perihelion. The tidal bulges raised by the sun are the greatest at perihelion, and so is the tendency for the planet's minimum inertial axis to align itself with the sun. What happens during the rest of Mercury's orbit is of less importance.

As Mercury was despun, it passed through a series of stages when its minimum inertial axis was aligned with the sun during every perihelion passage, but moved out of alignment when the planet was elsewhere in its orbit. This situation would have occurred every time the ratio of Mercury's orbital period to its rotational period (P/p) was just $n/2$, where n is one of the integers. Each of these times of resonant periods represented a quasi-stable rotational state for Mercury, and there was a tendency for the planet to remain in that mode of motion and not to be despun further.

However, as Mercury was despun through the higher resonance states $(P/p = \ldots \frac{6}{2}, \frac{5}{2}, \frac{4}{2})$, the rotational period continued to be significantly larger than the period of orbital revolution, so the forces of tidal deceleration sketched in Fig. 2-10 continued to slow the planet's rotation, preventing it from "locking into" any of these resonant rotation states. Only when Mercury's rotation had slowed to $P/p = \frac{3}{2}$ was the rotation rate of the planet (degrees/second) at perihelion almost as small as its rate of orbital revolution (degrees/second). Under these conditions Mercury's tidal bulge points almost directly at the sun; since rotation does not cause it to lag, the sun's attraction of the bulge does not torque the planet and further check its rotation.* Mercury has remained in this stable rotation state since.

It appears that a curious and complex form of spin–orbit coupling relates the slow retrograde rotation of Venus to the orbital periods of Venus *and* Earth. The orbital period of Venus is less than that of Earth (Table 2-1), since Venus is closer to the sun. Venus circles the sun 2.6 times while Earth completes just 1.6 circuits. Thus Venus passes Earth on the inside track, so to speak, once every 1.6 Earth years. Every time this happens, Venus presents the same face to the Earth. Presumably, Venus's minimum inertial axis is aligned with Earth at this

---

*Because of Mercury's substantial eccentricity (0.206), its rate of orbital revolution at aphelion is only about half what it is at perihelion (note the dependence of v on r in Eq. (2-3)). Away from perihelion, Mercury's rotation rate *is* greater than its rate of orbital revolution; but because the planet is then farther from the sun, the diminished force of tidal interactions is not sufficient to break the spin–orbit "lock" established at perihelion and further slow the planet's rotation. Such a condition did not occur when the moon was despun, because its orbit is less eccentric (e is currently 0.055). Tidal deceleration was effective at all positions in the moon's orbit, and it was despun until the $P/p = \frac{2}{2}$ resonance was reached.

time. Venus rotates exactly four times (from the point of view of an observer on Earth), in a retrograde direction, during the 1.6 years between encounters. How such a peculiar form of spin–orbit coupling would have been established is not well understood.

COMETS AND ASTEROIDS

The small bodies of the solar system are treated separately in this chapter because most of what we know about them is connected with their motions, and because they do not fit naturally into the chapters that deal with properties of the nine principal planets. The comets and asteroids form two discrete groups on the basis of their appearance and their orbits.

Asteroids appear as points of light in the telescope; they are small chunks of rock reflecting the sunlight that falls on them. Comets have a fuzzy, nebulous appearance (Fig. 2-13). All that we can see of them is a ball of sunlit gas and dust, effectively a transient atmosphere.

The orbital inclinations and eccentricities of planets, asteroids, and comets are plotted in Fig. 2-14, which is intended to display the regularity (or lack of it) of orbits. Perfectly circular orbits, lying in the ecliptic plane, would plot at the origin of the figure; the more an orbit departs from these regular conditions,

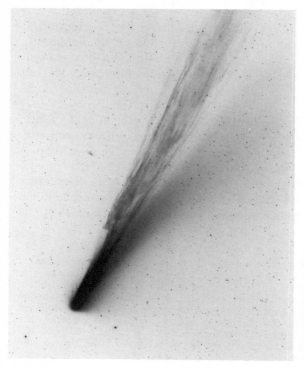

FIG. 2-13 Negative image of Comet Mrkos 1957d, in which the distinction between the two types of comet tails is especially marked. The constricted gas tail (above) streams straight away from the sun. The curved, diffuse tail at lower right consists of dust particles. The sense of motion of the comet in this plate is actually upward and to the left. Hale Observatories photograph.

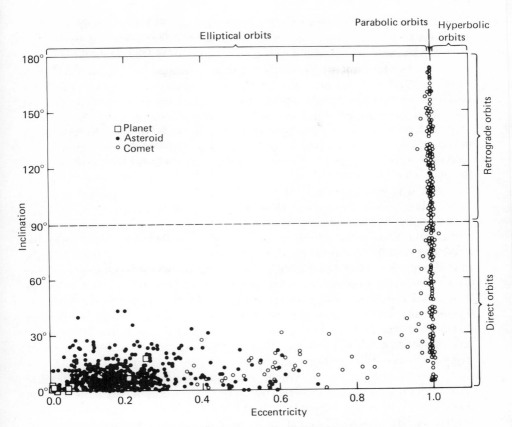

FIG. 2-14 Orbital eccentricities and inclinations of the planets, asteroids, and comets. About half of the comets and one third of the asteroids for which orbits are known are plotted. The belt asteroids appear as a dense cluster to the left, the near-parabolic comets as a column to the right; the space between contains Apollo and Amor asteroids and periodic comets, which have similar orbits.

the farther it plots from the origin. Although there is some overlap between the populations of asteroids and comets, for the most part they form two very distinct groups on the basis of their orbits.

Comets

The great majority of comets—those that form the vertical cluster at the right in Fig. 2-14—move in hairpin-like orbits that are nearly perfect parabolas. They come from vast distances in interstellar space, curve around the sun, and disappear again into the unknown. These *near-parabolic comets* come from all directions in space; they show no preference for the ecliptic plane or for direct motion about the sun (note the abundance of comets with high inclinations and retrograde orbits in Fig. 2-14). About four of these objects are observed to pass through the solar system in an average year.

In general only about one half of the near-parabolic comets will return to the solar system, and then only after an absence of thousands of years. The situation changes, however, if a near-parabolic comet passes near a large planet in the solar system and experiences a strong gravitational perturbation. This can have the effect of decreasing the eccentricity of the comet's orbit and placing it in a long-period elliptic orbit. During subsequent passes through the inner solar system, additional perturbations further reduce its eccentricity. The *periodic comets* that extend across the bottom of Fig. 2-14 are thought to have been derived from the near-parabolic group of comets in this fashion, after 20 to 1,000 passes through the solar system. Orbital periods of these "tamed" comets are generally 5 to 10 yr.

But why should periodic comets move in such well-behaved solar-system orbits (small inclinations, direct motion) if their source was the near-parabolic comet family, whose members move in all directions? It appears that planetary perturbations operate selectively in making periodic comets out of near-parabolic ones. The most likely way for a comet to be strongly perturbed is for it to remain in the neighborhood of Jupiter, the most massive planet in the solar system, for an appreciable period of time. This can only happen if the two bodies "fly in formation" (i.e., their orbital paths are close and near parallel) for a while; this in turn is possible only if the candidate near-parabolic comet is one that approaches the solar system with direct motion and almost in the plane of the ecliptic. More erratically orbiting near-parabolic comets have little chance of being perturbed into short-period orbits.

Comets are not usually visible when they are farther than about 3 AU from the sun; their nebulosity seems not to be generated until they move into the inner solar system. As they approach the sun, they become increasingly spectacular. A fully developed comet, near the sun, has the following visible components (Fig. 2-13):

A head, or coma, roughly spherical in shape, of gas and dust streaming outward; diameter, 10^5 to 10^6 km. The gas consists mostly of neutral molecules such as CN, C_2, NH, and OH.

A tail of ionized gas, up to 25×10^6 km long, streaming in an almost straight line radially away from the sun. (Comet "tails" do not trail behind their source comets like smoke from a rocket; they consistently move in a direction away from the sun. When a comet is outward bound, its tail precedes it.)

A tail of sunlit dust particles, again millions of kilometers long, again streaming outward from the sun, but often in a graceful curve. The dust particles are very small, ~ 0.1 micrometer (μm), and appear to consist largely of silicate minerals. Details of this sort can be read from the spectra of light emitted from or reflected by the component parts of comets.

At the center of each comet head is believed to be a lump of ice and dust, a conglomeration that has been likened to a "dirty snowball." The ice is largely the water ice we are familiar with; but other compounds or "ices" of carbon, nitrogen, oxygen, and hydrogen, which freeze only at very low temperatures, are probably also present. These cometary *nuclei* must be small (a few kilometers) and are not visible at all while they are in the cold outer reaches of the solar system. When they approach the sun's warmth, however, they come alive; the ices begin to sublime and the vapors to stream outward. In space the gas molecules are dissociated and ionized by solar energy.

As the icy nucleus of a comet wastes away, trapped dust particles are released and swept outward with the gases. Cometary nuclei are too small to be resolved in telescopes; they have only been glimpsed occasionally as bright points of light in the center of comet heads.

Once outstreaming cometary gases have been ionized, they interact with and are rapidly swept away by the solar wind (an unceasing flow of ionized gas emitted radially in all directions from the sun; Chapter 6), forming the comet's gas tail. Solar light pressure pushes fine cometary dust particles outward as well, but less vigorously: the attraction of solar gravity competes with the repulsive force of light pressure, and the resultant paths followed by dust particles produce the curve in dust tails.

Clearly, each comet has a finite lifetime; every time it approaches the sun a portion of it is irretrievably lost. After 100 to 1,000 (?) passes through the solar system, the comet's ices are gone. It is unclear whether the comet is totally dispersed at this point, or if a dead, dark core of nonvolatile mineral material is left in orbit.

Where do comets come from? They are not random wanderers in interstellar space, intercepted by the sun as it moves through the galaxy. If they were, interceptions would occur at various appreciable velocities, which means that the comets would then move through the solar system in hyperbolic orbits. The fact that new comets enter the solar system in near-parabolic orbits means their velocities at some great distance from the sun were almost zero; therefore, the comets were earlier moving through the galaxy *along with* the sun, although far from it. Thus the comets must be considered creatures of the solar system, however widely they are dispersed.

It is believed that the solar system is surrounded by a vast number of comets, as many as 10^{11} of them, in a cloud very roughly 50,000 AU in radius (Fig. 2-15). Normally, the comets coast in huge, slow, eccentric orbits about the sun, but from time to time a passing star gravitationally perturbs some of them, nudging a few toward the sun and starting them on long, plunging, near-parabolic paths to the inner solar system.

It has been postulated that all these 10^{11} comets and many more besides were created in the solar system when the planets were formed, and then perturbed by the planets out to their present positions. This aspect of the origin of the solar system is pursued further in Chapter 7.

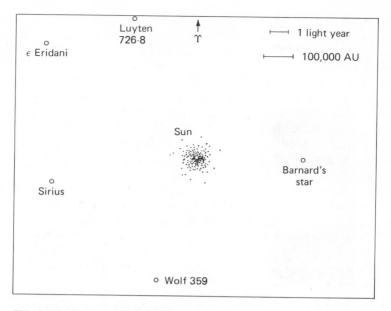

FIG. 2-15 The sun and the cloud of comets that moves with it through the galaxy. The scale of the comet cloud (dots) is shown relative to that of the spacing of stars in the sun's neighborhood. (Stars within 2.5 light-years of a plane through Earth's equator are shown.)

Asteroids

As already mentioned, asteroids are totally different from comets: they are sharply defined rocky masses that reflect sunlight; there is no hint of diffuse gassy envelopes surrounding them. It is possible to deduce the mineralogical character of asteroid surfaces from the spectra of sunlight reflected from them (Chapter 5). The minerals detected are principally silicates of the types abundant on Earth.

Many asteroids must be quite irregular in shape, because their brightness varies periodically, going through a maximum and minimum every few hours. This is most easily understood by picturing irregularly shaped asteroids that are rotating, so that large and small reflecting surfaces are alternately presented to Earth. The irregularity of asteroids, in turn, suggests that they are broken fragments. The great abundance and overlapping orbits of asteroids suggest that disruptive collisions must occur fairly frequently, and theoretical studies of collision probabilities bear this out.

There are no telescopic photographs showing the shapes of asteroids. They are so small and distant that, except in the rarest of circumstances, they appear only as points of light in telescopes. Their dimensions are deduced from their brightness, together with some knowledge of the reflecting power or *albedo* of their surfaces; the largest asteroid, Ceres, is ~1,020 km in diameter. Our best idea of the close-up appearance of an asteroid has come from photographs taken by the Mariner 9 and Viking spacecraft of the tiny moons of Mars. Phobos (Fig. 2-16), 28 km in long dimension, is comparable in size to many asteroids; like the asteroids, it is rocky in composition and irregular in form. The asteroids are undoubtedly pocked with impact craters, as Phobos is.

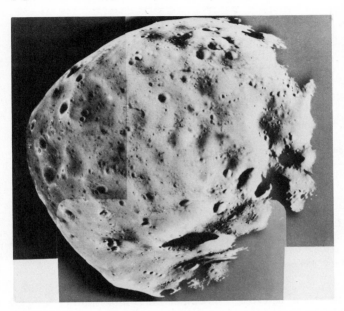

FIG. 2-16 Phobos, one of the two small satellites that orbit Mars, as photographed by the Viking 1 orbiter (1977). The satellite is ~20 km in diameter, roughly the size of the District of Columbia. The asteroids are thought to have a similar appearance; in fact, the Martian satellites may be captured asteroids. NASA photograph.

Orbits are known for about 2,000 asteroids. Many more than this are at large in the solar system, but below a certain dimension it becomes difficult or impossible to discover and track them from Earth. Also, how small does an object have to be before we call it a meteoroid or dust particle instead of an asteroid? Apparently, there is a continuous distribution of dimensions of small objects in the solar system from 1,000 km to less than 1 μm in diameter; and the smaller the size, the more numerous these objects are. Abundances of asteroids and asteroidal fragments are summarized in Table 2-2. Here the numbers of larger objects are those actually visible in telescopes, but the abundances of smaller fragments are estimates based on a projection of the size–abundance trend that holds for larger asteroids.

The orbits of asteroids are more nearly circular, less inclined, and generally "tamer" than those of comets, as Fig. 2-14 shows. (This figure is deceptive, incidentally, in that it seems to show the solar system populated with com-

Table 2-2 Dimensions and Numbers of Asteroids

The largest known asteroids:

Asteroid	Diameter (km)	Asteroid	Diameter (km)
CERES	~1,020	DAVIDA	~320
PALLAS	~610	CYBELE	~310
VESTA	~540	EUROPA	~290
HYGIEA	~450	PATIENTA	~270
EUPHROSYNE	~370	EUNOMIA	~270
INTERAMNIA	~350	PSYCHE	~250

In addition, there are:

Asteroids	Diameter
~200	>100 km
~2,000	>10 km
~500,000[a]	>1 km
~100,000,000,000[a]	>1 m

[a]Projections.

(*Data of D. Morrison and C. R. Chapman*)

parable numbers of asteroids and comets. It is important to remember that all the asteroids shown are constantly with us, orbiting between Mars and Jupiter, but only the periodic comets are permanent residents of the solar system. The numerous near-parabolic comets at the right of the figure live in interstellar space and only very occasionally dip into our planetary system.)

Figure 2-14 suggests some overlap between orbits of the asteroid and comet populations (those objects with eccentricities between 0.3 and 0.7). The mean distances of the orbits of periodic comets and the Amor and Apollo families of asteroids are also similar. (The Apollo asteroids, named for a 2-km type example, cross inside the orbit of Earth near perihelion. Apollo itself passed within 0.02 AU of Earth in 1932. Apollo asteroids have mean distances of 1 to 2.5 AU. Amor asteroids reach perihelion inside Mars's orbit, but outside Earth's. The great majority of asteroids, those that comprise the *asteroid belt*, have mean distances of 2.2 to 3.2 AU and do not even cross the orbit of Mars at perihelion.) Nonetheless, there are small differences in the orbital elements of comets and asteroids that allow them to be reliably differentiated.* The overall similarity in asteroid and comet orbits has prompted the suggestion that some

---

*In particular, Pe (period × eccentricity) is greater than 2.5 for comets and less than 2.5 for asteroids, with very few exceptions.

members of the two classes of objects are genetically related; Apollo asteroids may be the burnt-out cores of periodic comets, clumps of involatile silicates left after the ices were sublimed away. Such an origin is not reasonable for the belt asteroids, however, whose orbits are much less eccentric than those of periodic comets.

The angular shapes and vast number of belt asteroids, and the fact that they occupy a position in the solar system where the Titius–Bode law predicts the occurrence of a planet (Fig. 2-11), has led to the idea that asteroids are the debris of a disrupted planet. In recent years, however, this notion has been discredited: for one thing, it is hard to imagine what could have torn apart a solitary planet in that part of the solar system; for another, the meteorites, which appear to be samples of asteroids (Chapter 5), contain no mineralogical evidence of having once resided in the interior of a larger-than-asteroidal planet. Also, the orbits of the belt asteroids tend to be nearly circular and concentric; they do not cross over one another in a way that would suggest they all once originated from a point source. Finally, all the known asteroids do not add up to a large enough mass (i.e., only ~ 0.0002 of Earth's mass) to comprise an honest-to-goodness Titius–Bode planet.

The opinion currently prevalent is that there has always been a multiplicity of asteroids. There may have been innumerable asteroids, or only 10 or 20, at the beginning; a few of these may have survived intact, but the rest have been reduced by mutual collisions to the host of whirling fragments we see today.

Orbital periods of the belt asteroids are distributed between 3 and 7 yr, but not evenly (Fig. 2-17). There are jagged gaps in the distribution, particular

FIG. 2-17. Histogram of the periods of asteroid orbits. Arrows above show positions of orbits whose periods would be integral fractions of the orbit of Jupiter. Conspicuous gaps in the distribution of asteriods occur at periods $\frac{1}{3}$, $\frac{2}{5}$, $\frac{3}{7}$, and $\frac{1}{2}$ that of Jupiter.

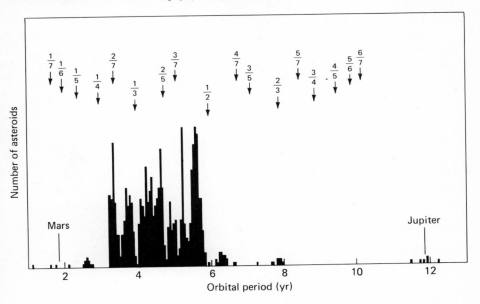

orbital periods that are unoccupied or thinly populated by asteroids. It turns out that these gaps correspond to periods that are integral fractions of the period of massive Jupiter, the next planet outward from the asteroid belt. If an asteroid's orbit should evolve so that its period falls at one of these critical values, it comes into resonance with Jupiter's orbit. This means the closest encounters between the asteroid and Jupiter come repeatedly when they are at the same positions in their respective orbits. Gravitational perturbations applied systematically like this are much more potent than they are if applied randomly, as is the case of two bodies in nonresonant orbits. Exactly what happens to asteroids in this circumstance is not fully understood, however. Asteroids have somehow been eliminated from orbits in $\frac{1}{4}$, $\frac{1}{3}$, $\frac{2}{5}$, $\frac{3}{7}$, and $\frac{1}{2}$ resonance with Jupiter's orbit, perhaps by being perturbed into other orbits with nonresonant periods; yet they have been concentrated at other resonances, such as $\frac{2}{3}$.

three

surfaces of planets

Our primary source of information about a planet is the way its surface appears—through a telescope, or to cameras in an orbiting spacecraft, or to explorers walking on it. The Jovian planets and Venus offer no solid surfaces to view, only layers of clouds; so the present chapter will generalize about Earth, the moon, Mars, and Mercury, those dense objects of the inner solar system whose surfaces are accessible to view. The branch of space science that attempts to understand surface processes on terrestrial planets principally by the study of photographs taken from a distance is called *astrogeology*.

The chief processes that shape planetary surfaces can be categorized as follows:

Exogenic processes
    Impact cratering by meteoroids
Endogenic processes
    Volcanism
    Effects of mantle motions
    Effects of atmosphere and hydrosphere

The endogenic processes are the traditional subject matter of terrestrial geology. They will be considered only briefly in this chapter; the reader is referred to other books in the Foundations of Earth Science Series (Prentice-Hall, Inc., Englewood Cliffs, N.J.) for detailed treatments. Much of the present chapter will be devoted to a discussion of impact cratering, a process that is unfamiliar to most Earth scientists but which dominated the early evolution of planetary surfaces.

IMPACT CRATERING

As noted in Chapter 2, the solar system includes large and disorderly populations of asteroids and comets; collisions are constantly occurring between these small objects and the planets. In early times the solar system's content of loose debris was much greater than now (Chapter 7), and the bombardment of planetary surfaces was correspondingly more intense. The collision between a planet and an independently orbiting object (a *meteoroid*) is a very energetic event, and great damage is done to both protagonists.

As noted in Chapter 2, the collision velocity is equal to the intrinsic velocity of approach of the two objects* plus an additional amount of velocity imparted to the approaching meteoroid by the gravitational acceleration of the planet (equal to the planet's escape velocity). Consider a meteoroid that follows the orbit of an Apollo asteroid before it impacts Earth. The intrinsic difference in orbital velocities at encounter is ~ 5 km/sec, and escape velocity from Earth is 11.2 km/sec (Table 2-1); so the meteoroid enters Earth's atmosphere at ~ 16 km/sec. Collision velocities can be as high as 53.3 km/sec for a hypothetical retrograde, near-parabolic comet striking Earth, or as low as 2.4 km/sec for an object initially in circular geocentric orbit that is attracted to the moon. In the latter case the difference in orbital velocities can be almost zero; the minimum impact velocity cited is entirely due to the gravitational attraction of the moon and equal to the lunar escape velocity.

At a relative velocity of 16 km/sec, the kinetic energy of a meteoroid colliding with Earth is 1.3×10^{12} ergs/gram (g). Comparison with the chemical energy of TNT, 4.2×10^{10} ergs/g, demonstrates the meteoroid's potential for destruction. Unless the meteoroid is small enough to be decelerated by Earth's atmosphere (see Table 5-1), its impact with the rocky surface of Earth is violent enough to blast out a crater whose volume is thousands of times greater than that of the meteoroid. The meteoroid itself is torn apart and dispersed in small fragments along with the debris from the crater.

Weathering and erosion erase most impact craters from Earth's surface in a time that is short compared to the geologic time scale, so these features are rare on our planet. About 70 partially preserved craters or crater groups are known on Earth. Often erosion has removed all but the shattered root zone of an old crater. Such remnants are termed *astroblemes*. Terrestrial craters are most abundant on the Precambrian continental shields (Fig. 3-1), where rates of vertical movement and erosion are lowest and the rocks are oldest.

Where hydrospheric weathering and erosion are not operative, as on the moon and Mercury, the landscape is dominated by patterns of overlapping craters (Fig. 3-2), the cumulative effect of billions of years of bombardment by meteoroids.

---

*The vectorial difference of their orbital velocities.

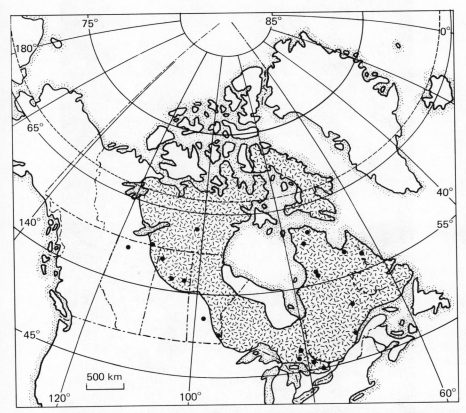

FIG. 3-1 Distribution of known impact structures (black dots) on the Precambrian Canadian Shield (dash-patterned area). These range in diameter from 2 to 56 km. Figure courtesy of M. R. Dence.

Simple Craters

Our knowledge of the cratering process has come mostly from laboratory simulations (in which projectiles are fired with velocities of up to 8 km/sec at various horizontal target surfaces), underground detonations of chemical and nuclear explosives, studies of terrestrial impact craters, and theoretical considerations.

Three stages of the cratering process are recognized: compression, excavation, and (especially in the case of large craters) subsequent modification. During the compression stage the meteoroid is engaging the target and compressing a small volume of target and meteoroid material near the point of impact. The kinetic energy of the meteoroid is transformed largely into compressional energy. During the excavation stage, the highly compressed system relaxes. A hemispherical shock or compressional wave radiates through the target, becoming less intense at it grows larger. Until it grows too large and

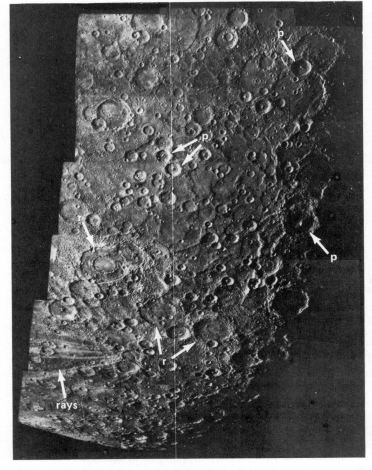

FIG. 3-2 (Above) Portion of the surface of Mercury, photographed by Mariner 10 (1974). The field of view is ~1,300 km high. Visible are simple craters, craters with central peaks (p) and central rings (r), and rays from a relatively recent crater. Rough terrain in the lower part of the figure is due to a dense peppering of small secondary craters surrounding the craters with central rings. NASA photograph.

FIG. 3-3 (Left) Laboratory experiment in which a projectile impacted an unconsolidated sand target surface in a vacuum chamber at 6.5 km/sec velocity. The field of view is 60 cm wide. The conical form of the ejecta spray shown (0.005 sec after impact) is maintained during later and more copious stages of excavation. Photograph courtesy of D. E. Gault and NASA Ames Research Center.

feeble, the shock wave is able to mobilize target material and propel it outward. The fluidized debris climbs the walls of a roughly conical cavity that is constantly growing, and is projected out of the cavity as a conical sheet (Fig. 3-3). Laboratory experiments indicate that only material from roughly the upper one third of the crater depth is propelled out of the crater; debris from the lower two thirds either never rises out of the crater or falls back into it. Figure 3-4 enlarges upon several aspects of the cratering process.

Simple impact craters (which are small on Earth, less than ~3 km in diameter) have an approximately bowl shaped form, with a depth that is about one fifth the diameter. An approximate relationship between projectile energy (E, in ergs) and the diameter (d) of the crater produced, which seems to hold for craters larger than ~1 km in diameter, is

$$d \simeq kE^{0.28} \tag{3-1}$$

where $k \simeq 2 \times 10^{-7}$ km/erg$^{0.28}$.

FIG. 3-4 Schematic cross section showing excavation of an impact crater. First a hemispherical shock wave propagates from the point where the initial compression of rock occurred (×); the lightest tone represents the highest pressures. The shock wave crushes target material and imparts radial motion to it (white arrows). Then, as the shock peak passes each element of rock and pressure diminishes, the negative pressure gradient decelerates the motion of that element. The deceleration does not simply halt or reverse the original acceleration, however; it also imparts an outward component of motion to each rock element, as suggested by the black arrows. The mobilized rock debris climbs the walls of a growing cavity and is ejected in a conical sheet.

In the model depicted, a horizontally stratified (A, B, C) target is cratered. During the earliest and most energetic stages of excavation, only the uppermost bed (A) is affected; debris from A is cast great distances. Later, debris from A and B are thrown lesser distances from the enlarged cavity. The last and least energetic stage of excavation involves strata A, B, and C. Some of this mixed debris is piled on the rim of the crater; some does not make it out of the hole, but slumps back onto the floor of the crater. Thus an inverted stratigraphy is established in the ejecta blanket surrounding the crater, in that debris from highest in the target volume tends to be deposited first and so occurs deepest within the ejecta deposit.

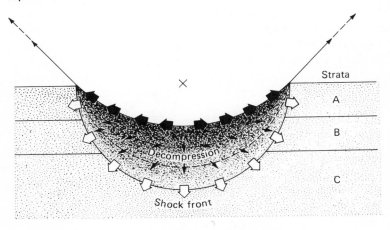

FIG. 3-5 The Arizona Meteor Crater, a well-preserved and dramatically exposed impact structure on Earth. Diameter is 1.2 km ; depth to surface of alluvial fill inside it, ∼100 m. Photograph courtesy of D. J. Roddy and the U.S. Geological Survey.

The classic terrestrial example of a simple impact crater occurs near Flagstaff, Arizona. The Arizona Meteor Crater (Figs. 3-5 and 3-6) is ∼1 km in diameter and ∼100 m deep. The surrounding desert is strewn with fragments of a particular type of iron meteorite, as well as crushed debris from the Permian and Triassic sedimentary beds that were impacted. Studies of the level of radioactivity in the meteorites show that the impact occurred at least 2,700 years ago.*

The crater is bowl shaped (Fig. 3-6), but is half-filled by rock debris (breccia) that slumped back into it after the last low-energy phase of excavation. The breccia is covered by layers of alluvium that the rain has since washed down into the basin. The impacted beds of sedimentary rock, which are elsewhere flat lying, are bulged upward around the crater rim and in places are even folded completely back. The thick debris blanket close in to the crater displays inverted stratigraphy, as predicted in Fig. 3-4.

---

*The particular radioactivity measured was induced in the meteorite by cosmic rays while it was in space. Once the meteorite is on Earth and shielded from cosmic rays by the atmosphere, its radioactivity begins to decline. The amount remaining is a measure of the meteorite's time on Earth.

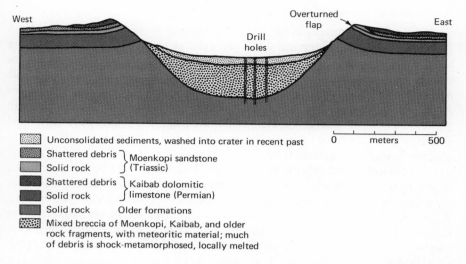

West

Overturned
flap

East

Drill
holes

0   meters   500

Unconsolidated sediments, washed into crater in recent past

Shattered debris ⎫ Moenkopi sandstone
Solid rock   ⎭ (Triassic)

Shattered debris ⎫ Kaibab dolomitic
Solid rock   ⎭ limestone (Permian)

Solid rock   Older formations

Mixed breccia of Moenkopi, Kaibab, and older
rock fragments, with meteoritic material; much
of debris is shock-metamorphosed, locally melted

FIG. 3-6 (Above) Cross section of Meteor Crater, Arizona; no vertical exaggeration. After E.
M. Shoemaker in B. M. Middlehurst and G. P. Kuiper, eds., *The Solar System*, v. 4, 1963 301–336,
University of Chicago Press.

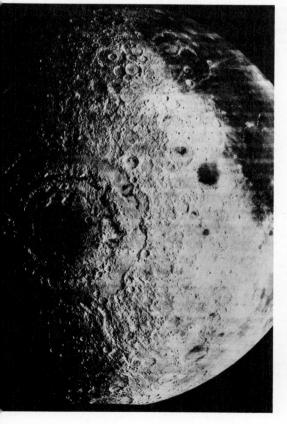

FIG. 3-7 (Left) The Orientale Basin,
a huge multiringed impact structure on
the western limb of the moon, as
photographed by Lunar Orbiter IV
(1967). Diameter of the outermost ring
is 900 km. Visible in upper right is
Oceanus Procellarum, one of the vast,
dark, lava-filled basins (maria) that
dominate the Earth-facing side of the
moon. Only small amounts of lava have
flowed into the Orientale Basin. NASA
photograph.

Complex Craters

Craters substantially larger than the Arizona Meteor Crater do not have simple bowl-like forms, but are shallower (relative to their diameters) and more complex in structure. This is especially evident on the moon and Mercury, where craters are abundant and well displayed. There the smallest craters have simple bowl-like forms, larger craters tend to have central peaks, and still larger craters have a ring or cluster of central peaks (Fig. 3-2; look for these features in Fig. 1-5 as well). The largest craters of all, the huge basins that were later filled or partly filled by vast basaltic lava flows (maria), display strikingly regular concentric ringed structures (Fig. 3-7).

These differing forms displayed by very large craters are believed to be due to gravitational readjustments of the surrounding target rock during and after the cratering event (the third stage of the cratering process, mentioned earlier). A hole in the ground is, of course, out of hydrostatic equilibrium. That is, if the hole were in a substance without strength, like water, it would immediately fill in and level out. If a crater in a planet is small, the strength of the surrounding rock

FIG. 3-8 Impact craters are bowl shaped during their excavation (A), and small craters remain so subsequently. Larger craters undergo modifications in shape as the rock surrounding them shears and slumps or flows to partly fill the crater cavity, probably immediately after the cratering event. The flow and crowding together of debris at the crater axis may raise a mound that persists (B); this is believed to account for the central peaks displayed by some craters (Fig. 3-2). Very large craters appear to readjust via inward faulting of coherent concentric blocks (C), forming multiringed basins (Fig. 3-7). Processes sketched are greatly simplified and idealized.

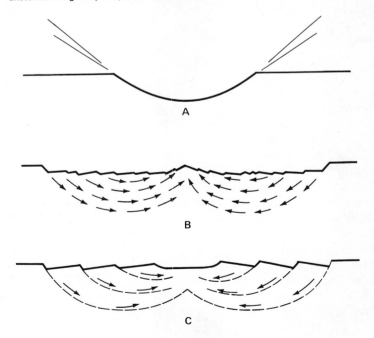

suffices to support the walls and keep the hole from slumping in. If the crater is very large and deep, however, the stresses beneath the crater walls can exceed the strength of the rock; the rock then fractures and flows down, inward, and then upward, partly filling the crater (Fig. 3-8).

Complex craters are known on Earth, moon, Mars, and Mercury. The critical diameter beneath which craters are simple and above which they are complex differs on these bodies; it is ~ 3 km for Earth but larger (10 to 30 km) in the case of the smaller planets. This is due at least in part to differences in gravitational acceleration at the surfaces of the various planets. The feebler gravity is, the higher crater walls can be without crushing the rock beneath them and slumping in, and so the larger craters can be, and still remain "simple."

Impact Melts

Crater-forming impacts on Earth are violent enough to melt portions of the target rock near the point of impact. In the case of small craters (such as the Arizona Meteor Crater), the melted rock appears as glassy bombs and lumps of slag in the ejecta blanket, and as masses of glass and finely crystalline rock mingled with the breccias in the floor of the crater. Craters larger than a few kilometers in diameter are often found to contain sheets of fine-grained igneous rock tens of meters or more thick. The composition of this melt rock tends to be similar to that of the local country rock, which appears to have been melted wholesale by the energy of impact.

Rock produced by the solidification of impact melts is abundant in the heavily cratered lunar highlands. This is evident from studies of lunar landforms, and also from the character of many of the samples collected by the Apollo astronauts in the highlands (Chapter 5).

Ejecta Blankets

Debris ejected from a small crater, such as the Arizona Meteor Crater, is deposited as a well-defined layer on the surrounding ground surface. The ejecta blanket is thick and continuous near the crater rim, becoming thinner and more patchy with distance. In the case of a very large crater, however, more than simple surface deposition is involved. Crater debris is projected great distances and impacts the surface at high velocities, excavating small *secondary craters*. There is a tendency for the primary-crater debris to mingle with and be diluted by the debris from the secondary craters. No simple interface, above which is crater ejecta and beneath which is the undisturbed planetary surface, can be recognized.

The great impact events that blasted the major ringed basins in the moon must have thrown out vast sheets of debris, but it is probable that most of this material mingled with and was effectively lost in the indigenous surface material where it fell. Only very close in to the basins (for a distance of perhaps one additional basin radius beyond the actual basin rim) was such a thickness of

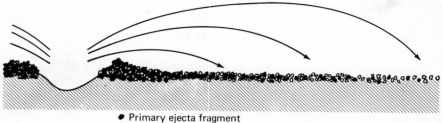

● Primary ejecta fragment

○ Secondary ejecta fragment

FIG. 3-9 Components of the ejecta blanket surrounding a large crater (schematic). High-velocity ejecta fragments, which travel farthest from the crater (right), hit hard and excavate secondary craters; primary ejecta is mingled with and lost in more abundant secondary crater debris. Low-velocity primary ejecta is deposited in large amounts near the original crater (left), overwhelming the secondary debris that is stirred up.

basin debris deposited that it was able to overwhelm and cover the local surface material (Fig. 3-9).

Cratered Terrains

The longer a planetary surface is exposed to bombardment by interplanetary meteoroids, the more densely cratered it becomes (unless, as on Earth, processes of erosion outstrip the rate of cratering). The density of craters is then a useful measure of the age of a planetary surface. Clearly, the maria are substantially younger than the highlands of the moon (dark versus light areas in Fig. 3-7).

Crater densities (or frequencies) are measured by literally counting the numbers of craters in various diameter ranges that are visible on a photograph representing a known area on a planetary surface. Several ways of representing the results of crater counts have been adopted; one way is shown in Fig. 3-10. The cumulative frequency/diameter plot has been used extensively in the literature of lunar photogeology, although it has certain weaknesses.* Each point in the plot expresses the frequency of craters *of that particular diameter or larger* per square kilometer of planetary surface in the area surveyed.

The caption of Fig. 3-10 explains the nature of such a plot. Craters of various sizes are imprinted on a fresh surface in proportions expressed by a production curve, the slope of which is established by the proportions of large and small meteoroids bombarding the surface. As more and more craters of all sizes accumulate on the surface, the production curve rises in the diagram. Where it rises above the 100 percent saturation curve, however, the production

---

*For example, the cumulative nature of the plot tends to suppress irregularities of the crater distribution that might be of importance. Anomalously scarce or abundant craters in a particular size range appear as minor steps in the frequency curve, not as troughs or peaks.

curve becomes meaningless, as it calls for a greater density of craters than can be fitted into a surface area.

In practice, the actual observed curve of crater frequencies often displays two segments with different slopes, as in the example of Fig. 3-10. The right segment (large craters, which accumulate relatively slowly) tends to parallel the production curve. With time and additional cratering, it will rise higher and higher in the diagram. The left segment (small craters, which accumulate rapidly) has saturated the surface, establishing a curve parallel to the 100 percent saturation curve. This segment of the curve will never rise higher, because a state of saturation has been achieved where every new small crater obliterates (on the average) one old small crater. It has been found that this state of crater *equilibrium* occurs not at the 100 percent saturation curve, which represents an artificial geometrically close packed array of craters of uniform size, but parallel to it, at a position representing ∼3 percent of saturation.

FIG. 3-10 Cumulative crater frequencies on a mare surface of the moon (dots) as measured in Lunar Orbiter photographs. Each dot records the number of craters of a given size *or larger* observed per unit area. Two other types of curves are shown for reference. (1) The *100 percent saturation curve* expresses the absolute maximum density of craters of a particular size that can be fitted side by side into an area, for a range of sizes. Curves representing 10 and 1 percent of this limiting density are also entered. (2) The steeper, solid line is a *production curve*: it represents the frequency/diameter relationship expected to be imprinted on a surface bombarded by a meteoroid population consisting of debris from fragmented asteroids, which would be heavily biased toward small fragments. As time passes and more craters of all dimensions accumulate, the production curve rises in the figure, but remains parallel to the curve shown. After D. E. Gault, *Radio Sci.*, v. 5, 1970, 273–291.

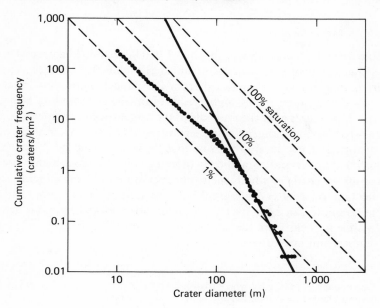

If the left segment of the distribution curve is static and the right segment rises with time, the inflection point or break in slope between them must migrate to the right with time. The older a surface, the larger the crater diameter at which the inflection in the crater frequency distribution appears.

The concept of crater equilibration explains an apparent paradox about the lunar maria. These appear smooth and nearly pristine from a distance (Fig. 3-7); yet the Apollo astronauts found them to be covered with a meters-deep layer of fine rock debris that had been pulverized and extensively mixed by cratering activity. The maria are similar in this respect to the much more obviously cratered highlands. In fact, the maria are equilibrated surfaces so far as meter-sized craters are concerned, and these generated the rock debris; but the maria are still so far from being equilibrated with large craters that they appear smooth from a distance. The older highland surfaces, on the other hand, are equilibrated over a wide range of crater diameters.

It is easy to deduce the relative ages of surfaces on a given planet from crater frequencies. Attempts have also been made to derive absolute ages by calculating how long it would take a given meteoroid flux (such as that observed to fall on Earth) to produce an observed crater frequency distribution; but whenever these estimates have been checked (in particular, by radiometric dating of samples from the lunar maria), they have usually turned out to be wrong. The reason is that the meteoroid bombardment has not been constant with time. More recently, the reverse has been done: crater counts on radiometrically dated lunar surfaces have been used to deduce the variation with time of the meteoroid flux (Fig. 5-25).

Shock Metamorphism

Extremely high pressures, as much as 1,000 kilobars* (kbar), are developed when a meteoroid of substantial size impacts a planetary surface. The high-pressure regime propagates outward from the impact point as a shock wave (Fig. 3-4), visiting momentary high pressures on the surrounding target rock. These shock pressures alter the minerals of the target rock in characteristic ways. In the 50- to 500-kbar range of shock pressures, the structures of minerals tend to be distorted. They develop microscopically visible lamellae, "kink bands," and twins that are crystallographically oriented (Fig. 3-11). At higher pressures, the minerals are partly or wholly melted or decomposed. Some minerals (quartz, graphite) take on new crystallographic forms during shock compression; for example, graphite can be converted to diamond. Shocked minerals are abundantly visible in rocks from the near vicinity of terrestrial impact craters and in lunar samples and meteorites.

---

*One kilobar = 1,000 bars, where 1 bar is a pressure of 10^6 dyne/cm², very nearly equal to atmospheric pressure on Earth (1 atm = 1.0132 bars).

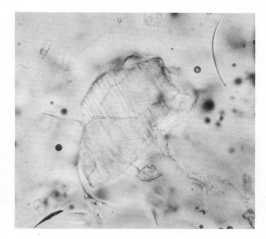

FIG. 3-11 Photomicrograph of a fragment of quartz displaying planar structure (lamellae) induced by hypervelocity impact. Width of field, 150 μm. The quartz is embedded in glass melted by the same impact. From an ejecta deposit associated with the Ries Kessel, a 20-km-diameter, 15 million year old impact structure in southern Germany. Smithsonian Astrophysical Observatory photograph.

ENDOGENIC PROCESSES

Volcanism

All the terrestrial planets with visible surfaces display areas covered with smooth plains (Figs. 3-2, 3-7, and 3-12), many of which have been interpreted as lava flows. Earth and Mars, in addition, display volcanic peaks. Oceanographic

FIG. 3-12 A portion of the surface of Mars (displayed as a mosaic of Mariner 9 photographs assembled on a 6-ft-diameter globe). The vertical extent of the image spans $\sim$3,000 km. Visible are smooth plains (lower half of the image), presumably volcanic flows; volcanic peaks (major blemishes to the left); arrays of nearly parallel fault scarps (top center); and the "headwaters" of a tributary to Valles Marineris (lower right). NASA photograph.

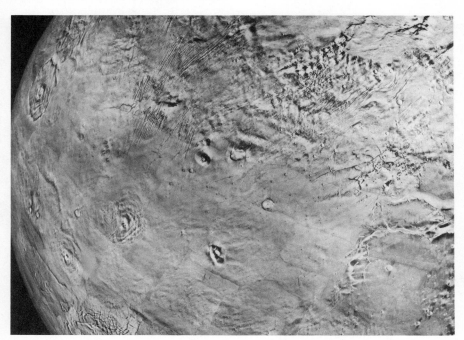

studies have shown that the ocean basins of the Earth are underlain by basaltic volcanic rock; the recent program of lunar exploration has shown that the lunar maria also consist of basalt flows (Chapter 5). Remote analyses of the surfaces of Mars and some asteroids (see Multispectral Photometry, below) indicate the presence of basaltic rock on these bodies. The Martian soils analyzed by automated instruments in the Viking landers have compositions consistent with a derivation by weathering from rocks of basaltic composition. Some of the meteorites are basaltic in character (Chapter 5).

Basaltic lava is understood to be produced by the partial melting of ultramafic rock in the mantle of a planet. Basalt is overwhelmingly the most abundant volcanic rock type on Earth and the moon. Lava of this composition, which has a relatively low viscosity, gives rise to characteristic landforms when it erupts in large quantities, spreads over the surface of a planet, and solidifies (e.g., see Fig. 3-13).

FIG. 3-13 A portion of the surface of Mare Imbrium on the moon. Lava flowing in a sheet from south to north $\sim 3 \times 10^9$ years ago got no farther than this area, where it solidified. The frozen lava flow front is still visible as an irregular scarp tens of meters high. NASA photograph.

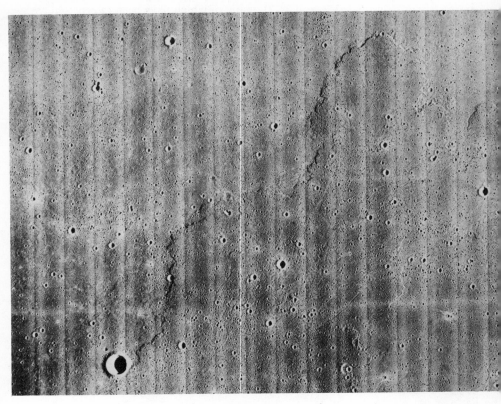

0   km   20

Effects of Mantle Motions

It is believed that the outward flow of heat from Earth's interior causes slow convective overturn of the plastic (yet solid) portion of the mantle. This rolling motion of the upper mantle material appears to keep the outermost rigid shell of Earth (the lithosphere; Chapter 4) in a fragmented state, and continually shifts the lithospheric plates around relative to one another. Characteristic landforms are produced at the plate boundaries: oceanic ridges (of basaltic rock) where plate margins diverge; oceanic trenches, island arcs, and folded mountain ranges where the plates encroach on one another. These features, all of which are linear in character, are prominent on a map of Earth (Fig. 3-18).

Mars also displays linear patterns of faulting (Fig. 3-12), which are believed to have been caused by the tensional effects of an upwelling motion of the mantle. However, landforms attributable to mantle motions are conspicuously absent on the smaller terrestrial planets, Mercury and the moon. The pattern of topography in the rugged portions of these bodies is almost entirely produced by overlapping impact craters.

Effects of Atmosphere and Hydrosphere

These agents have had a profound effect in shaping the surface of Earth. Apart from their actual physical presence in the form of oceans, polar ice caps, and clouds, Earth's atmosphere and hydrosphere are constantly at work tearing down the rocky substance of the terrestrial crust, moving the debris to new positions, and redepositing it. Much of the surface of Earth is covered by layers of sedimentary rock (Fig. 3-18).

Effects of this type have not been noted on the moon and Mercury, the airless small planets; but the surface of Mars has been profoundly modified by its atmosphere and, seemingly, by motions of water. Complex dry channels (Fig. 3-14), present in a number of areas on the Martian surface, are strikingly similar to terrestrial river channels; it is difficult to escape the conclusion that they were eroded by flowing water. Two possible sources for the water are indicated. Some Martian channels originate in hummocky, disorganized terrain (Fig. 3-15); it has been proposed that subsurface permafrost deposits once underlay these regions, and that melting of the ice produced a temporary flow of water that carved the stream channels. Slumping due to loss of the subsurface ice may be responsible for the chaotic landscapes in these regions. Other channels originate in such complex patterns of small tributaries that collection of rainfall from a broad drainage basin is suggested. However, present conditions on Mars make it very difficult to understand how any of these features could actually have been produced by flowing water; the pressure of water vapor in the Martian atmosphere is much too low to permit the existence of liquid water on the surface of the planet (Chapter 4). If a glass of water were spilled on the Martian surface it would freeze, then evaporate into the arid atmosphere, and would not subsequently precipitate as liquid water.

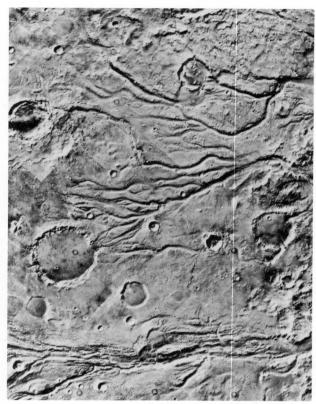

FIG. 3-14 (Left) Stream channels on Mars, photographed by the Viking I Orbiter (1976). NASA photograph.

FIG. 3-15 (Right) "Fretted terrain" on Mars; Mariner 9 photograph (1972). Width of field, 800 km. An old cratered upland surface (left) is separated from a younger, smooth lowland surface (right) by cliffs 1 to 2 km high. Mesa-like upland remnants stud the lowland plain. The cliff recession that produced this landscape is speculatively attributed to undermining of cliff faces by evaporation of subsurface ice exposed in them, with subsequent removal of slumped rocky debris by windstorms or water erosion. NASA photograph.

FIG. 3-16 Windblown terrain on Mars. Mariner 9 (1972); width of field, 250 km. Light streaks that point downwind from crater rims and other protuberances consist of dust deposited (or protected from erosion) in the lee of these obstacles. NASA photograph.

The thin Martian atmosphere is subject to violent windstorms that modify the surface of the planet by eroding its rocky substance, transporting the dust, and depositing it in layers elsewhere (Fig. 3-16). The Mariner 9 spacecraft arrived at Mars in 1971 during a violent duststorm that blocked a view of the surface features for three months. Surface photographs taken by the Viking spacecraft show windblown sand dunes along with abundant rocky fragments, presumably crater debris (Fig. 1-3).

The surface distribution of cratered and volcanic terrains, and landscapes modified by mantle motions and the effects of atmosphere and hydrosphere, is shown for the four mappable planets of the inner solar system in Figs. 3-17 through 3-20. All maps are Mercator projections extending from latitude 65°N to 65°S, but of course the scales are very different. It is not practical to map the same types of geologic units on all four objects because the processes that have affected them differ so greatly, and because our knowledge of them varies so much.

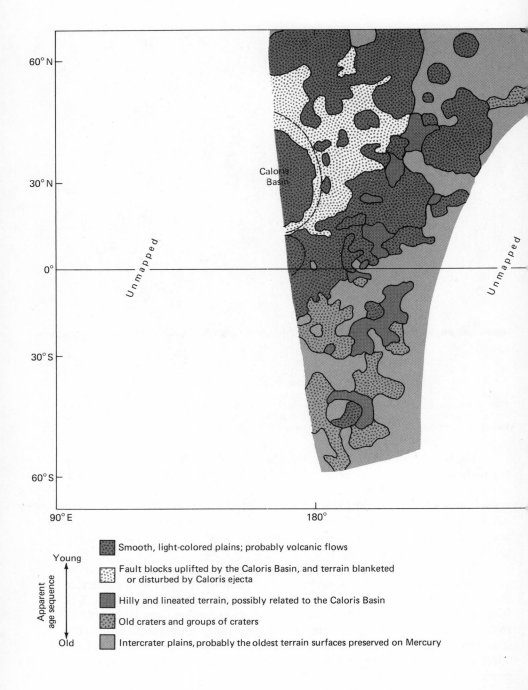

60° N

30° N

0°

30° S

60° S

90° E   180°

Caloris
Basin

Unmapped

Unmapped

Young

Apparent
age sequence

Old

Smooth, light-colored plains; probably volcanic flows

Fault blocks uplifted by the Caloris Basin, and terrain blanketed
 or disturbed by Caloris ejecta

Hilly and lineated terrain, possibly related to the Caloris Basin

Old craters and groups of craters

Intercrater plains, probably the oldest terrain surfaces preserved on Mercury

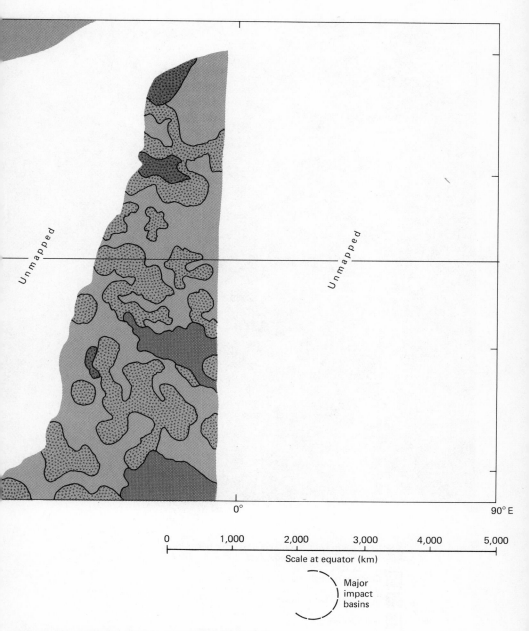

FIG. 3-17 Geologic map of a portion of Mercury, from photographs made by the Mariner 10 spacecraft. "Unmapped" regions were not illuminated or not visible to the spacecraft during the two passes that it made by Mercury. After N. J. Trask and J. E. Guest, *J. Geophys. Res.*, v. 80, 1975, 2461–2477.

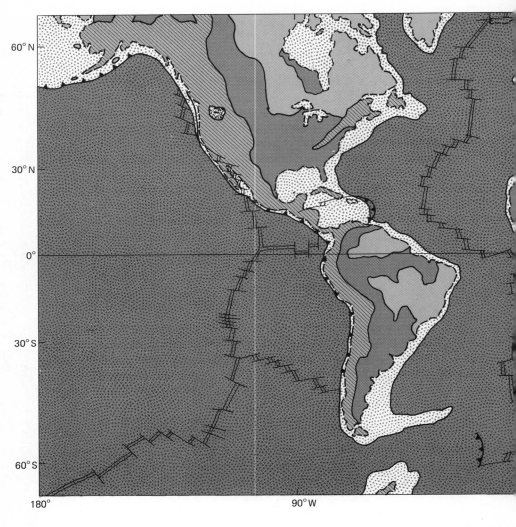

Young   Deep ocean basins, containing volcanic basalt flows
           covered by oceanic sediments

Various ages

     Continental shelves and shallow seas

     Continental basalt flows

     Sedimentary rocks

     Tectonic zones: rock folded and faulted by motions of
          Earth's crust

Old   Continental shields: deeply eroded, stable platforms of
           ancient rock of various types

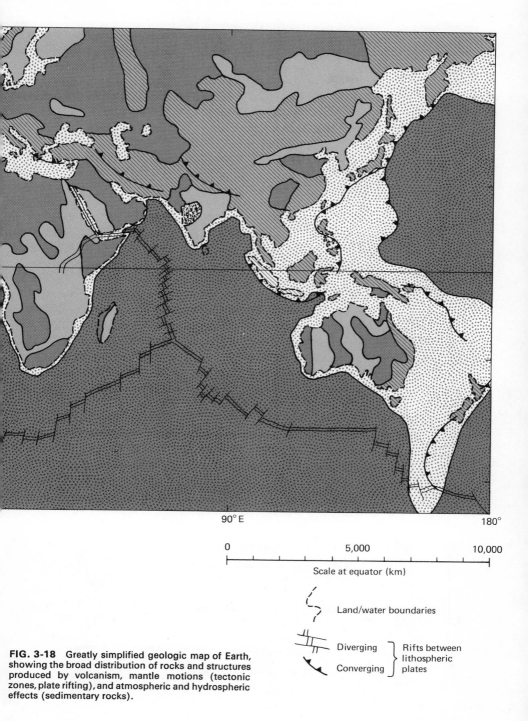

90° E   180°

0   5,000   10,000

Scale at equator (km)

Land/water boundaries

Diverging   } Rifts between
               lithospheric
Converging   } plates

FIG. 3-18 Greatly simplified geologic map of Earth,
showing the broad distribution of rocks and structures
produced by volcanism, mantle motions (tectonic
zones, plate rifting), and atmospheric and hydrospheric
effects (sedimentary rocks).

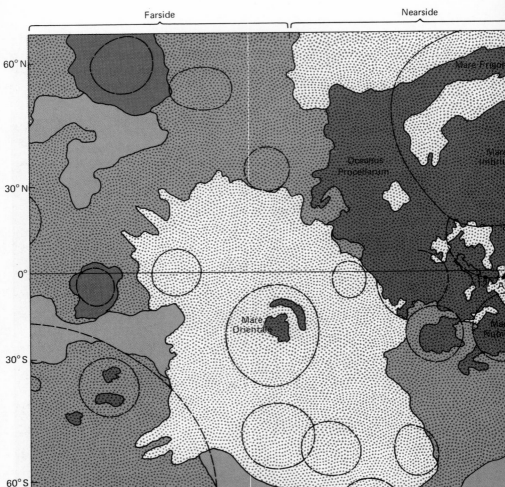

60° N

Maré Frigor

Mare
Imbriu

Oceanus
Procellarum

30° N

0°

A

Mare
Orientale

Mare
Nutr

30° S

60° S

180°   90° W

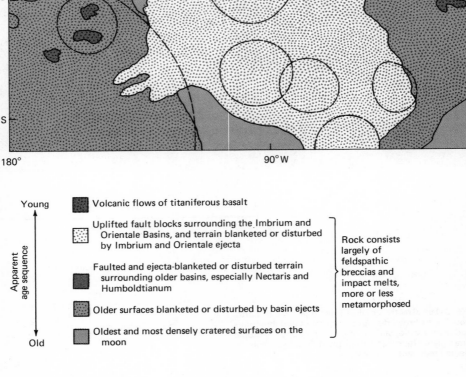

Young

Apparent age sequence

Old

Volcanic flows of titaniferous basalt

Uplifted fault blocks surrounding the Imbrium and
Orientale Basins, and terrain blanketed or disturbed
by Imbrium and Orientale ejecta

Faulted and ejecta-blanketed or disturbed terrain
surrounding older basins, especially Nectaris and
Humboldtianum

Older surfaces blanketed or disturbed by basin ejects

Oldest and most densely cratered surfaces on the
moon

Rock consists
largely of
feldspathic
breccias and
impact melts,
more or less
metamorphosed

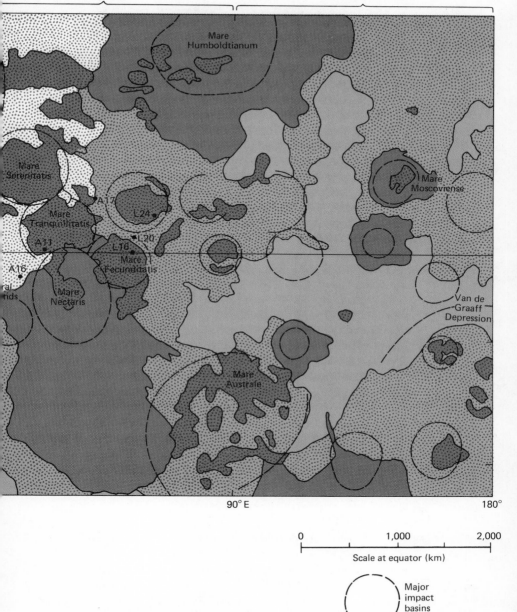

Mare
Humboldtianum

Mare
Serenitatis

Mare
Moscoviense

A17
L24

Mare
Tranquilitatis

L20

A11

L16

Mare
Fecunditatis

A16

al
nds

Mare
Nectaris

Van de
Graaff
Depression

Mare
Australe

90° E   180°

0   1,000   2,000

Scale at equator (km)

Major
impact
basins

FIG. 3-19 Geologic map of the moon compiled largely from photographs taken by orbiting spacecraft and ground-based telescopes. Samples have been returned to Earth from points A11-17 and L16-24 by the U.S. Apollo and the Soviet Luna missions. After K. A. Howard, D. E. Wilhelms, and D. H. Scott, *Rev. Geophys.*, v. 12, 1974, 309–327.

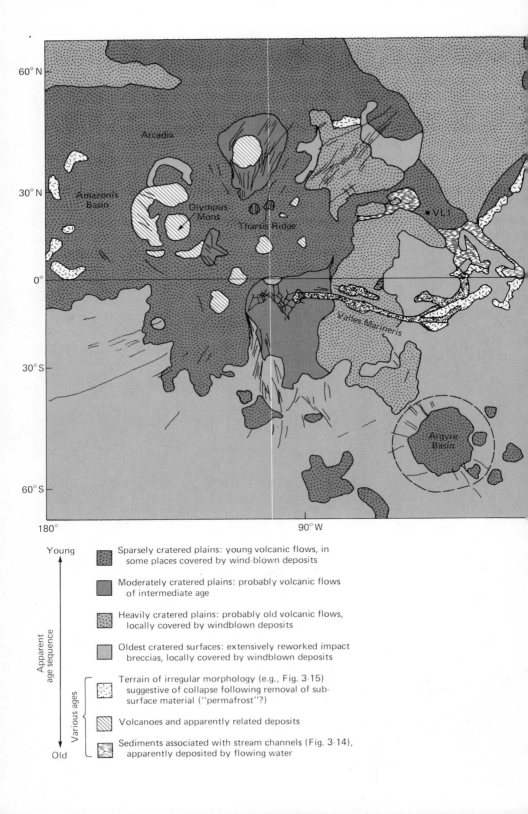

Young

Sparsely cratered plains: young volcanic flows, in some places covered by wind-blown deposits

Moderately cratered plains: probably volcanic flows of intermediate age

Heavily cratered plains: probably old volcanic flows, locally covered by windblown deposits

Oldest cratered surfaces: extensively reworked impact breccias, locally covered by windblown deposits

Terrain of irregular morphology (e.g., Fig. 3-15) suggestive of collapse following removal of subsurface material ("permafrost"?)

Volcanoes and apparently related deposits

Sediments associated with stream channels (Fig. 3-14), apparently deposited by flowing water

Apparent age sequence

Various ages

Old

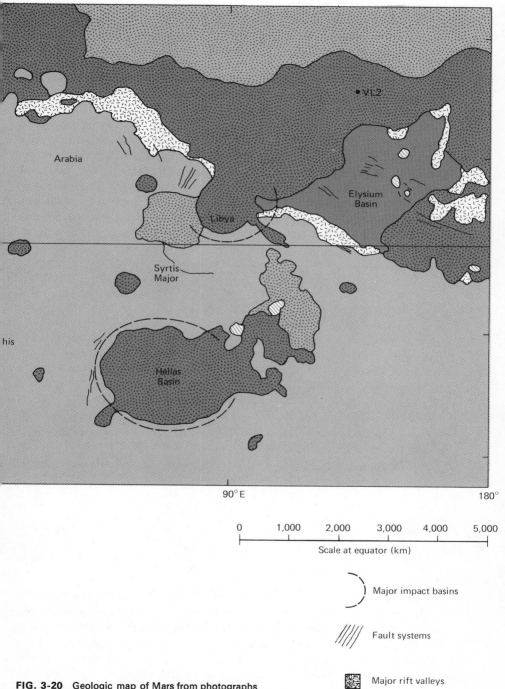

FIG. 3-20 Geologic map of Mars from photographs taken by the orbiting Mariner 9 spacecraft. VL1 and VL2: positions of the Viking 1 and 2 landers. After M. H. Carr, H. Masursky, and R. S. Saunders, *J. Geophys. Res.*, v. 78, 1973, 4031–4036.

MULTISPECTRAL PHOTOMETRY

The preceding discussions have dwelt on surface morphologies of planets, usually as viewed from a distance, and on inferred processes. Can anything be learned remotely about the chemistry or mineralogy of a planetary surface from the character of the light reflected by it?

Most minerals do not reflect totally as do mirrors; they are more or less transparent, and light impinging on them passes into crystals, where it is scattered and reflected from internal surfaces. In the process light is absorbed selectively, in that the electronic structures of the ions (especially Fe^{2+}, Ti^{3+}, and Ti^{4+}) in the minerals block certain wavelengths and pass others. The fraction of the original incident light that is eventually reemitted (reflected) at the surface of a transparent mineral has a spectrum that expresses the character of the mineral or minerals that reflected it.

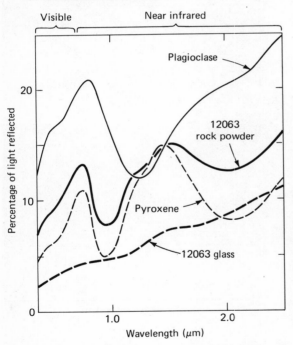

FIG. 3-21 Reflection spectra of mineral, rock, and glass powders. 12063 is a lunar basalt consisting largely of pyroxene, plagioclase, and ilmenite. Note that a powder of glass made by melting 12063 is less reflectant (darker) than a powder of crystalline 12063. The transition metal ions (especially Fe^{2+}, Ti^{3+}, and Ti^{4+}) absorb more efficiently when dispersed in glass than when concentrated in ilmenite and pyroxene crystals. After T. B. McCord and J. B. Adams, *Moon*, v. 7, 1973, 453–474.

The reflection spectra of lunar pyroxene* and plagioclase are shown in Fig. 3-21. A powder of lunar basalt, composed largely of these two minerals, has a spectrum with intermediate properties; but the spectrum of a glass prepared by melting the same basalt is almost devoid of the peaks and valleys that characterize mineral and rock powders. It can be seen that reflection spectra contain valuable information about the mineralogy of the reflecting surfaces. The

---

*A glossary of mineral terms appears at the end of the book.

spectra in Fig. 3-21 were measured in the laboratory, but similar spectra can be obtained for minerals that lie on a distant planetary surface by passing the light from a telescope image into the same type of instrument (a spectrophotometer) that is used to measure reflection spectra in the laboratory.

This technique has been exploited to learn about the planets that we have not been able to sample directly and to extend our coverage of the moon. Multispectral photometry has made possible regional mapping of the major basalt units in the lunar maria, and has demonstrated that the surface material of Mars is primarily oxidized basalt (the lighter areas consisting of more highly oxidized and, apparently, more finely divided dust). Use of this technique has also correlated the surface compositions of many asteroids with the mineralogical properties of the meteorites that fall to Earth (Chapter 5).

VENUS

The foregoing sections have omitted mention of Venus, second largest of the terrestrial planets and Earth's closest neighbor. This is because Venus's surface is totally obscured by dense clouds and not accessible to view. Our only impression of its surface morphology has come from Earth-based radar studies (Fig. 3-22). Some of these reveal the presence of circular, crater-like features, as well as linear features suggestive of mountains and rift valleys.

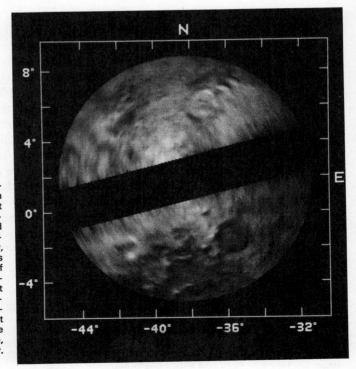

FIG. 3-22 Earth-based radar image of a small portion of the surface of Venus (not the whole disk of the planet) ; degrees of latitude and longitude are shown. Diameter of circular field of view, 1,400 km. The black bar is an artifact of the method of observation. Brightest regions are those that most efficiently reflect radar signals. Several circular structures, suggestive of impact craters, are visible. Figure courtesy of R. M. Goldstein, Jet Propulsion Laboratory. NASA photograph.

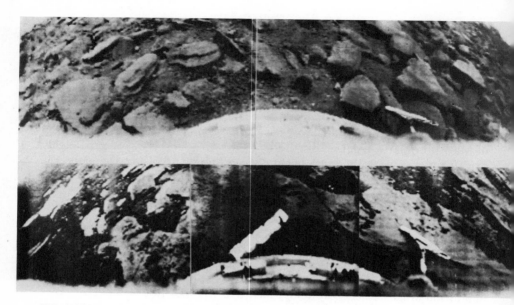

FIG. 3-23 Angular rocky debris on the surface of Venus (480°C !) as seen by panoramic television camera on the Soviet spacecraft Venera 9 (above), and what appear to be exposures of bedrock visible to Venera 10 (below), in 1975. Figures courtesy of the Academy of Sciences, U.S.S.R.

At first the apparent presence of large craters is somewhat surprising. Erosion by Earth's atmosphere and hydrosphere keeps our planet wiped almost clean of impact craters; surely the Venus atmosphere, hot and a hundred times as massive as Earth's, is an even more effective erosive agent?

Apparently not. Close-up photographs (Fig. 3-23) returned from the surface of Venus by two remarkable Soviet spacecraft that landed there are similar to the Viking photographs of the Martian surface (Fig. 1-3), in that they show an abundance of angular rock fragments. Two randomly placed observations on Earth's land areas or the moon would be more likely to show finer dust and gravel—rock comminuted by hydrospheric erosion in the case of Earth or by small meteorite impacts on the moon. Evidently, the hot dry Venus atmosphere protects the surface of that planet exceptionally well from these destructive processes, so that rock fragments retain their size and angularity for a long time.* If this is the case, impact craters may be better preserved on Venus than anywhere else in the solar system, and it is likely that the rubble shown in the Venera photographs is crater ejecta.

―――――――

*The same could be said for Mars, but less forcefully. The Martian atmosphere is not as dry as Venus's, yet much drier than Earth's atmosphere, which tolerates the existence of liquid water. It is not as dense as the Venus atmosphere, yet is dense enough to shield the Martian surface from impacts of the smaller meteoroids that are an important erosive agent on the naked lunar surface. The boulders strewn on the Martian surface (Fig. 1-3) may also be impact debris fragments.

The Soviet Venera 8, 9, and 10 landers measured levels of radioactivity due to the decay of U, Th, and ^{40}K in the rocks at three points on the surface of Venus. The activity found is attributable to ~2 parts per million (ppm) U, ~6.5 ppm Th, and ~4 percent K (Venera 8); ~0.6 ppm U, ~3.6 ppm Th, and ~0.5 percent K (Venera 9); and ~0.5 ppm U, ~0.7 ppm Th, and ~0.3 percent K (Venera 10). In addition, Venera 10 was able to determine a mass density of ~2.8 g/cm^3 for the rock analyzed. Properties of the rock at the Venera 9 and Venera 10 landing sites are comparable to those of terrestrial basalts; the Venera 8 composition corresponds more closely to that of a terrestrial granodiorite.

four

planetary interiors
and atmospheres

INTERIORS OF THE TERRESTRIAL PLANETS

The deepest exploratory drill hole penetrates 6 km into Earth, only 0.1 percent of the distance to the center of our planet. This might suggest that the interior compositions of the planets will always remain a mystery, but there are certain observations that can be made and conclusions that can be drawn. Observations and conclusions will be considered separately in this chapter.

Observations of Body Properties

The most fundamental properties of planets that can be measured are their dimensions and masses. Diameters can be measured in telescope images; more accurate values are obtained by radio occultation of spacecraft (the times are noted when radio signals cease to be received, and then resume transmission, from a precisely tracked spacecraft as it passes behind a planet). If a planet has a natural satellite, the planet's mass can be derived from the period and orbital mean distance of the satellite (using Eq. (2-1)). Failing this, the planetary mass can be calculated from the degree to which it gravitationally deflects the trajectory of a spacecraft sent near it. As a last resort, a planetary mass can be estimated from the long-term perturbations it causes in the orbits of neighboring planets. From their diameters and masses, the mean density of each planet can be calculated (Table 4-1).

A very informative body property of planets is the moment of inertia. The moment of inertia (I) of a body about any given axis is defined as

$$I = \int \rho r^2 \, dv$$

Table 4-1 Body Properties of the Planets

	Mass (× 10^{24} kg)	Equatorial Radius (km)	Mean Density (g/cm³)	Uncompressed Density (g/cm³)	Moment-of-Inertia Factor	Surface Magnetic Field (gammas)	Surface Temperature (°K)[a]
MERCURY	0.33	2,439	5.42	5.4	?	220	100–625[b]
VENUS	4.87	6,050	5.25	3.9–4.7	?	0–30	753
EARTH	5.97	6,378	5.52	4.0–4.5	0.331	31,000	295
MOON	0.073	1,738	3.34	3.3	0.392	<0.02	250
MARS	0.64	3,398	3.94	3.7–3.8	0.36–0.374	60	100–385[b]
JUPITER	1,900	71,900	1.31	—	0.25	402,000	134
SATURN	570	60,200	0.69	—	0.22	?	97
URANUS	87.6	25,400	1.31	—	0.23	?	60
NEPTUNE	103	24,750	1.67	—	0.29	?	57
PLUTO	?	~1,600	?	—	?	?	43 (?)

[a]Temperature of solid surfaces for terrestrial planets, cloud tops for Jovian planets.

[b]Nighttime and daytime temperatures.

where ρ is the mass density of the volume element dv, r is the nearest distance from the volume element to the axis about which the moment is taken, and the integration is over the whole volume of the body. It will be seen that the moment of inertia is an expression of the distribution of mass in the body; if the latter has a high-density layer near its surface, I has a larger value than it would have if this same high-density material were concentrated closer to the axis of the body.*

In describing planets, the moment-of-inertia factor, K, is often used, where $K = I/MR^2$, M being the mass of the planet and R its mean radius. This division yields a dimensionless number that is independent of the size or mean density of the planet; all it expresses is the interior distribution of mass, in terms of the tendency of relatively high density zones to be concentrated at deep or shallow levels. Examples of the moment-of-inertia factors of spheres with several interior configurations are given in Fig. 4-1.

The moment-of-inertia factor of a planet can be determined by observing how the latter is affected by rotation. Rotation has two effects on a planet. First, it flattens the planet's poles and bulges it at the equator; the degree of flattening

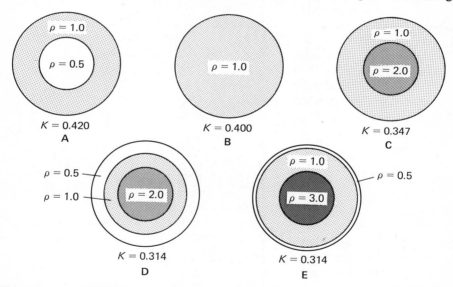

FIG. 4-1 Five examples of spherical bodies having different moment of inertia factors (K). K is independent of the size and mean density of a body; densities specified (ρ) are relative, not absolute values. Values of K in excess of 0.4 require higher densities near the surface than at the center of the body (e.g., model A), an unstable and improbable configuration. The density distribution is not uniquely defined by K; for example, models D and E are two of an infinite number of possible models for which $K = 0.314$.

*If the body does not have perfect spherical symmetry, I will vary depending upon how the reference axis is oriented in the body. Then there will be one particular axis orientation for which I is a minimum; this is the axis of inertia referred to in the discussion of spin–orbit coupling, Chapter 2.

can be measured in telescope images or by spacecraft occultations. Second, the spin-induced distortion of the planet causes a distortion of its gravitational field, such that the gravitational acceleration between the planet and an orbiting satellite is no longer strictly proportional to the inverse square of the distance between the two (an assumption that underlies all the equations of Chapter 2). The observable effect this has is to cause the long axis of the (elliptical) orbit of the satellite to slowly rotate about the planet.

The relationship between the visible flattening of a spinning planet and the distortion of its gravitational field depends upon the distribution of mass inside the planet (i.e., its moment-of-inertia factor), and this can be calculated if it can be assumed that the planet is in hydrostatic equilibrium (responds to gravity as if it were a fluid sphere). In practice, considerable uncertainty is attached to K for Mars because that planet is too small and strong to be well approximated by a fluid sphere. On the other hand, additional types of measurements that can be made of the motions of Earth and its moon make the assumption of hydrostatic equilibrium unnecessary in determining K for those objects. Mercury and Venus do not rotate rapidly enough to produce measurable effects of the type noted above; K has not been estimated for these planets.

Seismology provides additional important information about the interiors of those planets on which it has been possible to install seismometers. When an energetic event occurs on or in a planet, elastic waves propagate from the point of energy release to all other parts of the planet. (The energetic event may be a meteorite or spacecraft impact on the surface of the planet, or a deliberately placed explosive charge, or slippage along a fault plane inside a planet.) The time taken by a seismic wave in traveling from its point of origin to a distant seismometer station depends upon the seismic velocity or velocities of the rocky materials inside the planet through which the wave passes. The transmission of seismic waves from one event to one seismometer does not tell much; but when the signals from many seismic events, received at a network of seismometers, are analyzed simultaneously, it is possible to derive a *seismic velocity model* or profile for the interior of the planet. This reveals any gross pattern of layering that may exist in the planet, since seismic velocities tend to change abruptly at boundaries between layers having different chemical compositions or physical properties. It also indicates the seismic velocities within each layer, and these are additional clues as to the compositions of the layers.

Seismic velocity profiles for Earth are shown in Fig. 5-20 of *Structure of the Earth* by S. P. Clark, Jr., which also contains a comprehensive discussion of seismology as a tool for examining planetary interiors. The only planet other than Earth that has been studied seismologically at the time of writing is the moon; the seismic velocity model for the moon is shown in Fig. 4-2.

The *periods of free oscillation* of a planet are another source of information about the interior configuration of the body. Energetic events on or in a planet excite not only trains of seismic waves with a vibration period of a few seconds; they also promote gross oscillations of the planet as a whole (with periods of 70

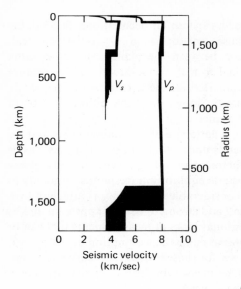

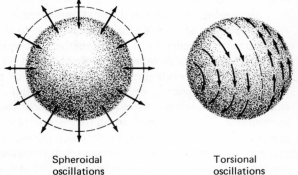

FIG. 4-2 (Left) The seismic velocity model of the moon most consistent with observed relationships between positions of energetic events and travel times to the recording seismometers. V_p, compressional wave velocities; V_s, shear wave velocities (shear waves are attenuated beneath ~ 700 km by nonrigidity of the lunar rock). Profiles are drawn as bands rather than lines, reflecting uncertainties. After Y. Nakamura et al., *Geophys. Res. Letters*, v. 1, 1974, 137–140.

FIG. 4-3 (Right) Simplest form of the two modes of free oscillation excited by a disturbance in an elastic sphere.

Spheroidal oscillations

Torsional oscillations

to 3,200 sec in the case of Earth). The two types of modes of free oscillation excited in spherical bodies are sketched in Fig. 4-3. The periods of free oscillation of a planet are an expression of the distribution of densities and seismic velocities within it.

Models of Planetary Interiors

What can these observations tell us about the actual composition and physical state of the interior of a planet? Different types of rock have characteristic mass densities and seismic velocities, but obviously it is not simply a matter of matching rock types to the planetary properties discussed above. There are several difficulties. First, the density and seismic velocities of a given rock type vary with temperature and pressure; allowance must be made for this when an attempt is made to match the physical properties of a material inside a planet to a particular rock type. Second, the correspondence between physical properties and composition is not unique; a series of rock types with different compositions can have essentially the same mass density and seismic velocities. Third, in the absence of seismic data, the distribution of mass densities inside a planet cannot be known unambiguously; a great many different internal arrangements of density can be imagined that would correspond to a particular planetary mean density and moment-of-inertia factor.

The problem is approached by setting up a model of the interior of a planet, one that seems reasonable from various points of view. After taking account of the effects of temperature and pressure inside this hypothetical planet, its mean density, moment-of-inertia factor, seismic velocity profiles, and periods of free oscillation are computed, and the results compared with reality. If there is gross disagreement, the model is discarded and a new one is tried. If there are minor deviations, adjustments are made in the model (positions of layer boundaries are shifted, material compositions altered), and the physical properties are recomputed. In this way interior models are arrived at that seem reasonable and are consistent with all that is known about a given planet. (It should always be borne in mind, however, that a particular model is not necessarily the only planetary configuration that would satisfy the observational data for a planet; nor is it necessarily correct.)

There would be an infinite number of acceptable models if we were free to choose among all the chemical elements in constructing model terrestrial planets. Fortunately, this is not the case; there are compelling reasons (from the compositions of the sun and meteorites; Chapters 5 and 6) for believing that the terrestrial planets are composed predominantly of a few elements: silicon, magnesium, iron, oxygen, and sulfur. When only these elements are allowed as the building blocks for model planets, the number of permissible models is drastically reduced, and we begin to gain insight into the character of planetary interiors, even if it is not possible to specify rock compositions with complete accuracy and confidence.

The more completely a planet's geophysical parameters have been studied, the less ambiguous is our picture of its internal composition. Each geophysical property (mean density, seismic velocity profile, etc.) amounts to a *constraint* on the composition of the planet; the more constraints there are, the more narrowly hedged in is the range of permissible models. Naturally the geophysical properties of Earth are best known of all the planets. All the planetary characteristics discussed above have been measured for Earth. These constraints have led to the model of Earth's interior shown in Fig. 4-4; there is relatively little ambiguity about the type of material that is needed at various depths to account for the observed geophysical properties of our planet.

Next best known is the moon; its density and moment-of-inertia factor are known, and seismometers placed by the Apollo astronauts have permitted seismic velocity profiles to be estimated (Fig. 4-2), although these are necessarily less precise than Earth's seismic velocity profiles, being based on a smaller network of seismometers and fewer energetic events. Only knowledge of the

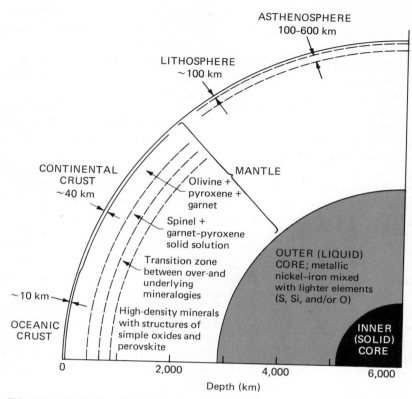

FIG. 4-4 Model of the earth's interior consistent with known geophysical and geochemical constraints. Layerings according to two different criteria are shown. The lower portion of the figure summarizes inferred mineralogical layerings; the upper part of the figure shows the division of the upper mantle into regimes with differing rigidities (lithosphere and asthenosphere). Both forms of internal structuring occur together over the entire earth. Mineralogical differences are chiefly due to the effect of pressure, rather than variability of chemical composition.

lunar periods of free oscillation are totally lacking. An interior model of the moon is shown in Fig. 4-5.

The density and approximate moment-of-inertia factor are known for Mars. Seismometers were emplaced by the Viking spacecraft; but since only one of these functioned, it has not been possible to derive information about the positions of major layer boundaries in the planet. In the absence of seismic information, a variety of models can be (and have been) postulated, all of which are consistent with the planet's mean density and moment-of-inertia factor (Fig. 4-6).

Least of all is known about Mercury and Venus. Since these planets do not have natural satellites, and since they rotate too slowly (Table 2-1) to be flattened perceptibly, there is no basis for estimating their moment-of-inertia factors; the only constraint that has to be satisfied in modeling these planets is that their mean densities must be accounted for. This leaves great latitude for the modelist.

The only basis for perceiving differences in overall chemical composition among the terrestrial planets comes from a comparison of their mean densities. The apparent densities of the planets are substantially different (Table 4-1), but this is due in part to differences in their dimensions: the larger a planet is, the higher are pressures in its interior, the more its internal substance is compressed, and so the greater its mean density becomes. To compare the intrinsic, composition-dependent densities of the planets, it is necessary to take out the effect of self-compression. This can be done, but not with great certainty, because the correction is model dependent; some planetary materials are more compressible than others. The "uncompressed densities" of Table 4-1 have been corrected

FIG. 4-5 Model of the lunar interior consistent with known geophysical and geological constraints. As in Fig. 4-4, the lower part of the diagram shows chemical stratifications, the upper part the boundary between lithosphere and asthenosphere; both types of layering are applicable over the whole moon. Mantle mineralogy is less variable in the moon than Earth, because the range of pressures experienced is much smaller. The distinction between upper and lower mantle is based on the seismic profile (Fig. 4-2); its basis in mineralogy is not known. Size (or, indeed, existence) and composition of the core are highly uncertain.

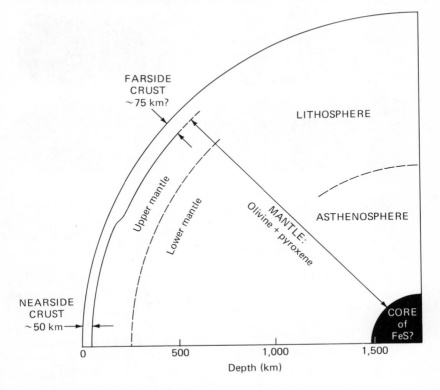

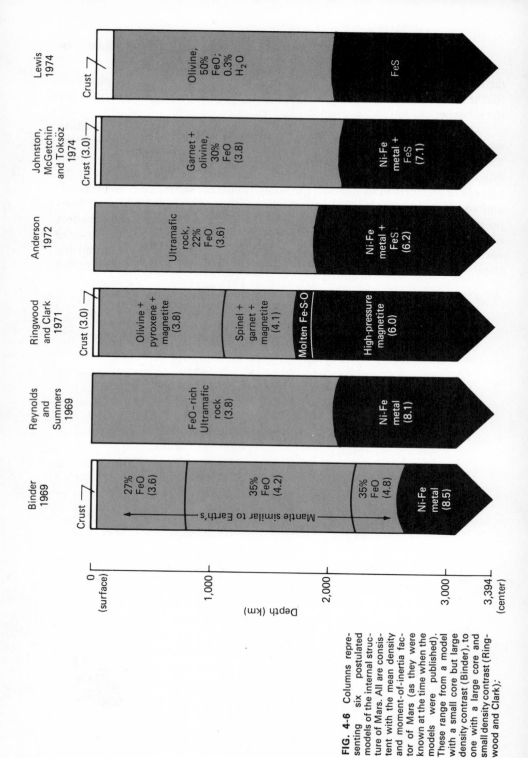

FIG. 4-6 Columns representing six postulated models of the internal structure of Mars. All are consistent with the mean density and moment-of-inertia factor of Mars (as they were known at the time when the models were published). These range from a model with a small core but large density contrast (Binder), to one with a large core and small density contrast (Ringwood and Clark):

74

according to the compressibilities of materials in model planets (like those of Figs. 4-4, 4-5, and 4-6) that fit within the constraints and seem reasonable. Where substantially different models of planetary structure have been proposed, ranges of uncompressed densities have been reported. In spite of uncertainties, it is clear that the intrinsic density of the material of terrestrial planets tends to decrease outward in the solar system.

Temperature Histories of Terrestrial Planets

The decay of radioactive elements in planets generates heat, which diffuses to the planetary surface where it is radiated away into space. The thermal history of a planet is a crucial element of its overall evolutionary pattern and its present state, since many if not most geologic processes are temperature dependent: igneous activity, geochemical differentiation, mantle convection and continental drift, the outgassing of an atmosphere, and core convection (the probable source of planetary magnetic fields). The estimation of geophysical properties of a particular model planet, discussed above, also depends on the present-day temperature profile assumed.

The thermal evolution of a planet can be followed mathematically, as sketched in Chapter 1, if the following information is at hand:

1. The initial thermal state of the planet, after its formation. It may have accreted slowly at low temperatures, or it may have been hot at the outset for any of a number of reasons: the dissipation of tidal stresses in its interior; the decay of short-lived radionuclides that might have been present when the solar system was formed but which have long since vanished (^{26}Al, with a half-life of $\sim 10^6$ years, is a prominent candidate); the deposition of energy by infalling planetesimals during formation of the planet by accretion; or the heating of the planetary interior by electric currents that may have been induced by an outward flow of plasma in the solar system, believed to have been shed by the sun at an early stage of its evolution (Chapter 7).

2. The amount and distribution of long-lived radioactive elements (U, Th, ^{40}K) in the planet.

3. The behavior of the substance of the planet at various temperatures. At low temperature, rock is stable and transmits heat by the familiar process of conduction. At temperatures just below melting, rock becomes slightly plastic in its properties, and can transfer heat by slow convective movements more efficiently than it can by conduction. Melting begins to occur in a given rock type above a particular temperature (the *solidus temperature*), and the magma generated is likely to percolate to higher levels in the planet. First-formed magma like this tends to incorporate most of the uranium, thorium, and potassium that was present in the parent rock; the migration of these heat-producing elements in the planet has an effect on its thermal history. Finally, wherever rock is extensively melted, the liquid can convect rapidly and is capable of extremely efficient and rapid heat transfer.

The thermal history of the moon can be followed with more confidence than that of any other planet, because studies of the lunar samples (Chapter 5) have provided insight into its initial thermal state: it appears that the outer layers of the moon to a depth of more than 100 km were melted at the outset. A computed thermal history for the moon, which takes this surface ocean of magma as a starting point, is shown in Fig. 4-7.

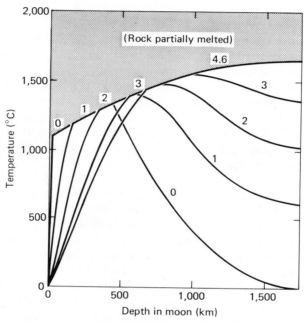

FIG. 4-7 Model thermal history of the moon (after M. N. Toksöz et al., *Moon*, v. 4, 1972, 190–213). Shaded area in the upper part of the diagram is at temperatures above which rock starts to melt. Temperature profiles are shown at five different times, ranging from the time of formation of the moon (0) to the present day (4.6×10^9 years, the age of the solar system). The initial thermal profile assumes high temperatures to a depth of 450 km, presumably generated by the energy of accretion of the moon. With the passage of time, outer layers of the moon cool by radiative losses to space, but the interior is heated by radioactive decay. Maximum temperatures are limited by the melting behavior of rock, since molten rock carries heat and radioactive elements toward the surface. The model is consistent with observed heat flow at the lunar surface, with the levels of uranium, thorium, and potassium observed in lunar samples, with the requirements for early melting of the moon to more than 100-km depth, and with present-day observations of a (presumably very hot) lunar asthenosphere (Fig. 4-5). First stages of the computation of this temperature history were similar to the calculated array shown in Fig. 1-6.

Rock Strength Versus Temperature

As mentioned above and in Chapter 3, rock becomes "soft" at high temperatures, in the sense that it yields and flows if stressed for very long periods of time. Thus a load (such as a mountain range) that is underlain by hot mantle rock will not be supported indefinitely; with time it sinks until it reaches a position of buoyant equilibrium, like a log floating in a millpond. This is the concept of *isostasy*, which is fundamental to terrestrial geophysics.

The outermost shell of a planet, which is relatively cool and therefore rigid, is termed the *lithosphere*. The warmer, more or less plastic zone* beneath it is named the *asthenosphere*. On Earth the lithosphere is only 50 to 200 km thick; this rigid shell tends to fracture, and fragments of it move about over the mobile asthenosphere (the concept of plane tectonics). The moon's lithosphere, on the other hand, is about 700 km thick, extending halfway to the center of that body (Fig. 4-5). This difference in lithospheric thickness is attributed to the moon's smaller size and therfore the greater ease with which heat is conducted to its surface, where it is radiated away into space. Being less able to conserve its inner warmth than Earth, a thicker layer of the moon has cooled to a state of rigidity. The massive lunar lithosphere is far too strong to be broken and moved by motions in the asthenosphere; there is no surface evidence of anything equivalent to plate tectonic motions on the moon.

Magnetic Fields of Planets

Earth's magnetic field appears to emanate from the core of our planet; it is generally thought to be caused by convective motions in the molten, electrically conductive substance of the outer core (Fig. 4-4), which are believed to redirect and amplify the feeble magnetic field of the galaxy (the regenerative dynamo theory). Beyond this general concept, the process is poorly understood. Essential ingredients appear to be a molten conductive core, something that causes movements of the core material, and planetary rotation (the near coincidence of Earth's magnetic poles and the rotation axis suggests an important relationship).

Space probes have measured the magnetic fields of most of the planets. The values obtained (Table 4-1), which are highly variable, are generally consistent with the dynamo theory. The only planet with a magnetic field known to be greater than Earth's is Jupiter, which rotates rapidly (once in 9.8 hr) and is believed to have a lower mantle composed of liquid metallic hydrogen, which would be convective and conductive just as the earth's core is (see the section on Jovian Planets later in this chapter). The weakness of the magnetic fields of Mercury, Venus, and the moon can be attributed to their slow rotation rates (Table 2-1). In addition, the moon's core is small (or nonexistent; Fig. 4-5) and possibly not hot enough to be molten.

On the other hand, the small magnetic field of Mars is somewhat puzzling, since this planet rotates once every 24.5 hr, probably has a core of some type (Fig. 4-6), and is large enough to have a hot interior (note the evidence of relatively recent volcanic activity on Mars's surface; Fig. 3-12).

---

*Nonrigid material of this sort does not transmit seismic shear waves (wave motions that amount to a side-to-side shaking of the rocky material) well. Shear waves that would have traversed a depth greater than ~700 km have not been observed in the moon (Fig. 4-2), which leads to the interpretation that the lunar asthenosphere begins at this depth (Fig. 4-5).

Asymmetry of Planets

In much of the preceding discussion, the planets have been treated as spherically symmetric bodies. However, this is true only as a first approximation. The basic asymmetry of our own planet is obvious; most of the land area of Earth falls in one hemisphere; the Pacific Ocean occupies practically all of the other hemisphere. More is involved than just a distinction between land and water: the low-density, chemically differentiated crust of the earth is five times thicker under the continents than it is under the ocean basins. The asymmetric configuration of Earth's crust is not a static condition; the continents are in motion over the surface of the mantle, and continually adopt new positions relative to one another.

Asymmetry is not a condition peculiar to Earth. The moon and Mars have been found to be asymmetric as well, although there is no evidence that their conditions of symmetry are in flux, as Earth's is. The moon's most obvious asymmetry is in the concentration of lava flows (maria) on one side (the Earth-facing hemisphere; Fig. 3-19). Again, however, this is the surface expression of a more profound asymmetry. Apollo spacecraft orbiting the center of mass of the moon, and monitoring their altitudes with laser altimeters, found the mean lunar surface is not a constant distance (radius) from the center of mass. The lunar farside stands some 5 km higher relative to the center of mass than the nearside surface. Thus the half of the moon's mass that lies on the near-Earth side of the moon's center of mass occupies a slightly smaller volume than the half that lies beyond the center of mass; therefore, the mean density of near-Earth lunar material must be slightly higher than that of farside material. This has been interpreted to mean that the lunar farside contains a larger component of low-density crustal material; the farside crust would have to be thicker than the nearside crust by about 75 versus 50 km. The systematically lower level of the lunar nearside surface invited the preferential eruption of lavas in that hemisphere.

Mars's asymmetry has been detected by a variety of measurements made by the Mariner 9 spacecraft and by Earth-based radar. The heavily cratered southern hemisphere of Mars ("Oldest cratered surfaces" of Fig. 3-20) was found to stand 3 to 4 km higher than the younger, relatively smooth volcanic plains in the north. Again, a difference in thickness of low-density crustal material is implied.

ATMOSPHERES OF THE TERRESTRIAL PLANETS

The thickness of an atmosphere cannot be expressed as can that of an ocean or a layer of rock, because it has no well-defined upper boundary. Instead, it thins progressively with altitude, ultimately merging with the space environment. The decrease of gas pressure (p) with height (z) is described approximately by the barometric law

$$p = p_0 e^{-z/H}$$

where p_0 is the ground-level pressure, and H, the *scale height*, is a parameter characteristic of the particular planetary atmosphere under consideration. (H is the distance one would have to rise in that atmosphere in order to experience a drop in atmospheric pressure to $1/e$ of its former value.) Surface temperatures and pressures and scale heights of the atmospheres of Venus, Earth, and Mars are given in Table 4-2.

Table 4-2 Physical and Chemical Properties of the Atmospheres of Terrestrial Planets

	Surface Temperature (°C)	Surface Pressure (atm)	Scale Height (km)	Mass of Atmosphere (kg/cm²)
VENUS	468	99	14.9	115
EARTH	15	1	8.4	1.03
MARS	−63	0.0052	10.6	0.016

MAJOR ATMOSPHERIC COMPONENTS
(percent by volume)

	CO_2	H_2O	N_2	O_2, O	Ar
VENUS	95	<1	<2	<0.1	?
EARTH	0.03	<1	78	21	0.9
MARS	95	<0.1	2–3	0.1–0.4	1–2

Atmospheres are not chemically static or homogeneous. Earth's atmosphere is almost so up to an altitude of ∼90 km; the principal exception to this is the tendency of water vapor in the atmosphere to precipitate in regimes of low temperature and high pressure. Above this height, two complications arise. (1) Gas molecules tend to be broken into constituent atoms (photodissociated) when energetic, short-wavelength solar radiation impinges on them. (This effect is diminished at lower altitudes, because the overlying atmosphere absorbs most of the short-wavelength radiation). These atoms, in turn, tend to recombine into molecules when they collide. (2) Stirring and mixing of the thin air at high altitudes is not as efficient as it is near Earth's surface; as a consequence, there is a tendency for the upper atmosphere to stratify according to the masses of the constituent gas atoms, such that the heavier (higher-molecular-weight) gases are concentrated in the lower part of the atmospheric column. At altitudes of 1,000 to 3,000 km, the (very thin) atmosphere contains a large proportion of the light gas helium; at higher altitudes, the (even thinner) atmosphere is enriched in hydrogen. Effectively, above ∼90 km altitude each gaseous species has its own scale height and behaves independently of the other species. The scale heights are inversely proportional to molecular weights of the gaseous species.

Escape of Atmospheres

Gravity tends to hold an atmosphere around its planet, but the atoms and molecules that comprise the atmosphere are in constant thermal motion, and if a particular atom or molecule has a thermal velocity greater than the escape velocity of the planet, it is in danger of being lost to space. For this to happen, of course, the atom or molecule in question must be moving in a generally upward direction, and must be high enough in the atmosphere that its outward flight is not likely to be obstructed by collisions with other molecules at higher levels. The atmospheric layer in which atoms and molecules are dispersed thinly enough to permit escape in this fashion is called the *exosphere*. Earth's exosphere lies 500 km and more above its surface.

At a given temperature T, the average thermal velocity of an atom or molecule of species i is

$$v_i = 2\sqrt{\frac{2kT}{\pi m_i}} \tag{4-1}$$

where m_i is the mass in grams of an atom or molecule of i, and k is the Boltzmann constant ($k = 1.38 \times 10^{-16}$ erg/°K). It can be seen that in a mixture of species the lighter atoms and molecules move more rapidly than the heavier ones. To a first approximation, those species for which v_i is greater than the escape velocity for a given planet will be lost promptly from that planet's atmosphere; other (heavier) species are retained.

In detail, it is not so simple. Atoms or molecules of a given species, at a particular temperature, do not move at a uniform velocity v_i, but over a range (termed a *Maxwell distribution*) of velocities for which the average is v_i. The velocity distributions for atoms of oxygen, helium, and hydrogen in a gas at 1,000°K are shown in Fig. 4-8. The important thing to see is that, at any given time, some members of species i are traveling at velocities greater than v_i. Therefore, even if v_i is less than the escape velocity from a planet, there is still some loss of species i from its atmosphere. The rate of loss may or may not be significant, depending on the magnitude of the difference between v_i and the escape velocity, and the shape of the velocity distribution curve. For the velocity distributions shown in Fig. 4-8, it is clear that hydrogen would be lost promptly from Venus (escape velocity, 10.4 km/sec), since ~ 1 percent of the hydrogen atoms in a gas mixture are moving at more than the escape velocity at any given time. The mean thermal velocity of helium is only 1.8 km/sec, yet a small fraction of the helium atoms ($\sim 10^{-10}$) move at more than 10.4 km/sec; so helium, too, would tend to escape from the Martian atmosphere at 1,000°K, but at a slow rate. The loss rate of oxygen is so many orders of magnitude less than that of helium that losses can be neglected.

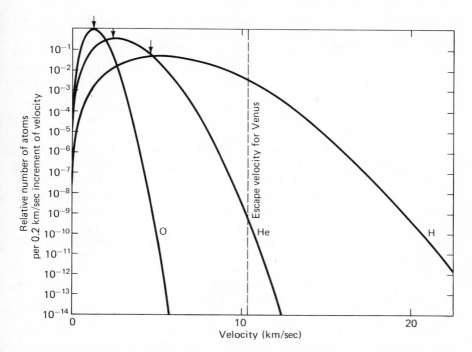

FIG. 4-8 The Maxwell distribution of velocities among atoms of three gases at 1,000°K. Arrows indicate the mean velocity (v_i) for atoms of each species. Note that the vertical axis, expressing relative abundances, is a logarithmic scale encompassing many factor of 10. Atoms of light gases are in more rapid motion that heavy gas atoms, so are more likely to escape from a planetary atmosphere into space. In the example shown, ~ 1 percent of the hydrogen atoms are moving at greater than the escape velocity of Venus, but only $\sim 3 \times 10^{-10}$ of the helium atoms are. At lower temperatures, all three curves would contract to smaller velocity ranges.

The rate of thermal loss of a given species from an atmosphere can be calculated. The escape rate is higher (1) the lighter the gaseous species, (2) the smaller the planet (because of the smaller escape velocity), and (3) the nearer the planet is to the sun (hence the higher the exospheric temperature, and so the greater the mean thermal velocity of gas atoms and molecules). Some species will have escaped entirely during the age of the solar system, others not. Hydrogen (H and H_2) would be lost from the atmosphere of the Earth, and hydrogen and helium from the atmospheres of Venus and Mars in 1 million yr. In 10 million yr, helium also escapes from Earth's atmosphere. Heavier species are expected to be retained, but it should be remembered that molecules of high atomic weight (such as CH_4, NH_3, and H_2O) are susceptible to photodissociation into their component atoms, of which the hydrogen is eligible for escape.

Some loss of atmospheric gases is also caused by the solar wind, a flow of ions that perpetually expands outward from the sun (Chapter 6). The solar wind ions stream pass Earth at ~ 400 km/sec, and clearly could knock gas atoms that they collide with away from Earth. However, the present solar wind flux is so small that this loss mechanism is relatively unimportant. (In addition, Earth's magnetic field tends to deflect the approaching solar wind ions, further reducing their effect on the atmosphere.) Early in the history of the solar system, on the other hand, the solar wind may have been very much more intense than it is now (Chapter 7), and this could have drastically modified early planetary atmospheres or removed them altogether.

Origin of Atmospheres

The planets are believed to have formed from a nebula of gas and dust having essentially the same composition as the sun (Chapter 7). Is it possible that the newly formed terrestrial planets gravitationally seized their first atmospheres from the gas of the nebula, and that these primordial atmospheres evolved by chemical reaction and exospheric escape into the present planetary atmospheres? Apparently not. The small abundance of noble gases (Ne, Ar, Kr, Xe) in Earth's atmosphere cannot be understood in terms of this model. Consider neon: all of this element that was present in the captured nebular gases should still be present in Earth's atmosphere, since neon is too heavy to escape and does not react with rocks of the solid Earth. Knowing the composition of the sun (Chapter 6), we can calculate the proportions of other gases that would have accompanied this much neon. Nitrogen, it turns out, has approximately the same abundance as neon in the sun ($N/Ne \cong 0.85$), so the amount of nebular nitrogen captured would have been about the same as the amount of neon. Yet we know that nitrogen is vastly more abundant in the present atmosphere than neon (40,000 times as abundant). This superfluity of nitrogen, which forms the bulk of our atmosphere, must have come from some other source. It is generally accepted that, if Earth ever had a substantial atmosphere of nebular composition, it has been largely lost, presumably stripped away by an early intense solar wind, as mentioned above. The present terrestrial atmosphere must have been produced almost entirely by outgassing from the rocks of Earth's interior. It is probably safe to extend this conclusion to Venus and Mars as well.

Compositions of Planetary Atmospheres

Atmospheric compositions are studied by direct chemical analysis and by Earth-based and spacecraft spectroscopy. The proportions of major atmospheric constituents of Venus, Earth, and Mars (best data at the time of writing) are given in Table 4-2. Mercury and the moon lack permanent atmospheres altogether, presumably as a result of thermal escape and interactions with the solar wind.

There are striking differences in the compositions and abundances of the atmospheres of Venus, Earth, and Mars; for example, the dominant atmospheric gas on Venus and Mars is carbon dioxide (CO_2); on Earth it is nitrogen (N_2). Does this variability reflect a fundamental difference in the chemical composition of the three planets, or can it be understood in terms of different processes acting on the same type of planetary raw materials? To compare atmospheric compositions perceptively, the data of Table 4-2 need to be recalculated. First, the actual amounts of atmospheric constituents (in kilograms per square centimeter of planetary surface) should be reckoned, in place of volume percentages. Second, oxygen should be eliminated from consideration, and the comparison limited to amounts of carbon, hydrogen, and nitrogen. This is because the small amounts of oxygen present in atmospheres, as elemental oxygen and oxide molecules, cannot be separated for consideration from the huge amounts of oxygen present in the silicate and oxide minerals that comprise the bodies of the planets; and an examination of differences in the gross state of oxidation of the terrestrial planets is beyond the scope of the question posed in the present section. (This larger question is touched upon in Chapter 7. The significance of oxygen in Earth's atmosphere is discussed below.)

Third, a comparison of the abundances of carbon, hydrogen, and nitrogen on the terrestrial planets has to include the amounts of these elements present in oceans and polar caps, incorporated in crustal rocks, and adsorbed or frozen out in the pores of the soil (so far as these can be estimated), as well as the amounts present in the gaseous atmospheres at any given time; there is constant cycling of these elements between atmospheres and the condensed states named.

Net abundances of carbon, hydrogen, and nitrogen recalculated along these lines are given in Table 4-3. In the case of Mars, allowance is made for a 1-km thickness of H_2O ice in the polar caps, but not for H_2O ice as permafrost or for condensed CO_2 or N_2.

Table 4-3   Carbon, Hydrogen, and Nitrogen Contained in Combined Atmospheres, Hydrosphere, Polar Caps, and Sediments of Planets

Planet	CARBON	HYDROGEN	NITROGEN
	\(kg/cm^2\)		
VENUS	30	<0.06	<1.5
EARTH	20.4	50	0.8
MARS	~0.004	~0.06	~4×10^{-4}

Comparison of Venus with Earth

When the terrestrial carbon incorporated in the biosphere, dissolved as carbon dioxide in the oceans, and buried in the form of carbonate rocks and fossil fuels is included in the carbon inventory of our planet, it turns out that there is no major difference in the abundance of this element on Venus and Earth (Table 4-3). The much greater mass of the Venusian atmosphere and its CO_2-rich character appear to be simply due to the fact that all of Venus's carbon is mobilized in its atmosphere as CO_2, whereas the great bulk of Earth's carbon is in the condensed state at any given time. (This assumes, of course, that there is no condensed carbon on Venus. There is unlikely to be any, in view of the high surface temperature on Venus, but the absence of condensed forms of carbon has not been established.)

Table 4-3 also shows that there is not necessarily a discrepency in nitrogen between the two planets. If the absolute amount of nitrogen present in the terrestrial atmosphere is also present on Venus, it is so highly diluted by the massive atmosphere of that planet as to be undetectable by the measurement techniques applied to Venus to date.

There is definitely a discrepancy in hydrogen, however, when the H_2O of Earth's oceans and hydrated rocks is included in the terrestrial hydrogen inventory. (Again, this assumes that the high Venusian surface temperature precludes the existence of hydrated rocks in that planet.) Two explanations have been offered for Venus's deficiency of H_2O. (1) The raw material from which Venus formed may have had an intrinsically lower content of H_2O then Earth's starting material. (2) H_2O originally present in the Venus atmosphere has been systematically photodissociated, after which the hydrogen escaped and oxygen was incorporated in the rocks of the planet (as a result of reactions with iron-bearing minerals). Earth's H_2O has been spared a similar fate by the fact that our atmospheric structure causes H_2O vapor to condense and precipitate at altitudes of a few kilometers; it has a hard time reaching the thin upper atmosphere where solar ultraviolet radiation causes photodissociation. (Precipitation occurs in the Venus atmosphere, too; indeed the planet is wholly shrouded in clouds (Fig. 4-9); but the condensate appears from spectral studies to be an aerosol of concentrated sulfuric acid, not water.)

FIG. 4-9 Cloud patterns on Venus, photographed in the ultraviolet by Mariner 10. At visible-light wavelengths, Venus appears as a relatively featureless disc. NASA photograph.

If explanation (2) is correct and there is no compelling evidence that the initial abundances of hydrogen, carbon, and nitrogen differed greatly between Venus and Earth, what aspect of their evolution led to the dramatic differences in compositions of the present-day atmospheres of these planets? The answer is not known with certainty, but an interesting model has been advanced that is based on the familiar comparison of planetary atmospheres with a greenhouse.

Atmospheric gases are relatively transparent to solar radiation, so the sun's energy penetrates them, warming the planetary surfaces beneath. The absorbed energy is reradiated by these surfaces, but at wavelengths longer than those of the original incoming solar radiation (i.e., the reradiation is at infrared wavelengths). Atmospheres are not very transparent to infrared radiation, so the passage of this radiant energy is impeded. As a consequence, heat builds up in the atmosphere and the planetary surface beneath it; the planetary surface may become substantially hotter than would be the case if it were exposed naked to the sun, without an atmosphere, at its customary position in the solar system. This process of heat entrapment has been nicknamed the *greenhouse effect*. The high temperature of the surface of Venus is undoubtedly produced by the greenhouse effect.

The degree of surface warming depends upon the opacity of the atmosphere to infrared radiation, and this in turn is directly related to the amount of CO_2 and H_2O vapor in the atmosphere, since these molecules are absorbers of infrared radiation. Water vapor is particularly opaque to infrared radiation.

If the amount of water vapor in an atmosphere increases with its temperature (as it would, of course: the maximum possible vapor pressure of H_2O is the saturation pressure, in excess of which H_2O condenses and rains out; and the saturation pressure increases with temperature), and if conversely the temperature increases with the H_2O vapor content of the atmosphere (because of the infrared opacity of H_2O molecules), we have the makings of a self-amplifying system—a *runaway greenhouse*. The way in which the H_2O vapor content of the atmospheres of Venus, Earth, and Mars may have evolved is shown in Fig. 4-10. In this model, liquid water is prevented from condensing on Venus by a runaway greenhouse. Consequently, all Venus's water joined the atmosphere of the planet, where with the passage of time it was photodissociated and the hydrogen was lost by exospheric escape, as was postulated earlier.*

Figure 4-10 implies that liquid water condensed on only one planet, Earth. This would mean that life could arise only on our planet, if we are correct in believing liquid water to be essential to the origin of life. (However, we should

---

*If the infrared opacity of water vapor in atmospheres is chiefly responsible for the greenhouse effect, how can Venus maintain a greenhouse once its H_2O has been dissociated and the hydrogen lost to space? Some other atmospheric constituent must block the escape of heat in this case. The sulfuric acid clouds of Venus are at least part of the answer; this compound is opaque in the infrared. The workings of the Venus atmosphere are far from being understood, however.

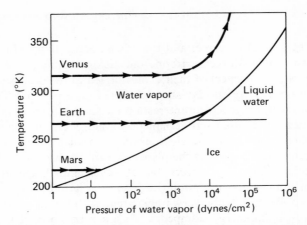

FIG. 4-10 A model that rationalizes differences in the evolution of atmospheres of Venus, Earth, and Mars. As H_2O vapor was evolved from the interiors of the three planets, the H_2O vapor pressure in their atmospheres built to higher and higher values (three tracks with arrows). Differences in starting temperatures for the three atmospheres are due to differences in proximity to the sun. When atmospheres accumulate more than $\sim 10^3$ dynes/cm² of H_2O vapor, the greenhouse effect begins to operate, raising the temperature of the atmosphere. But no more than ~ 20 dynes/cm² of H_2O vapor could accumulate in the Martian atmosphere; any additional H_2O vapor evolved from the interior of Mars froze out as ice on the surface. Similarly, H_2O vapor in excess of $\sim 10^4$ dynes/cm² in the terrestrial atmosphere condensed as liquid water. In the case of Venus, however, it has been suggested that increasing efficiency of the greenhouse effect (a "runaway greenhouse") prevented H_2O from ever condensing, no matter how much was added to the atmosphere. After S. I. Rasool and C. de Bergh, *Nature*, v. 226, 1970, 1037–1039.

keep in mind the Martian stream valleys that seem to require at least occasional flows of liquid water on that planet. Presumably, fluctuations of temperature at the surface of Mars periodically melt and liberate buried reservoirs of ice.) Life has modified the character of the terrestrial atmosphere drastically by photosynthetically dissociating CO_2. The oxygen produced is returned to the atmosphere; the carbon is incorporated in living matter, some of which is subsequently buried in sediments before it can decay and reoxidize. In this way major amounts of carbon have been taken out of circulation, and the oxygen that originally accompanied it (together with some oxygen from dissociated H_2O) has accumulated to a high concentration in the atmosphere.

It should be stressed that this separation of carbon and oxygen in the terrestrial system is chemically unstable, and is maintained only by the ceaseless efforts of green plants. In the absence of life the character of our atmosphere would change radically as carbon-bearing sedimentary rocks were eroded and exposed to oxidation. Free oxygen would be replaced by a mixture of CO_2 and CO, making the terrestrial atmosphere somewhat more similar to the atmospheres of Venus and Mars.

Comparison of Mars with Earth

The difference between absolute amounts of carbon, hydrogen, and nitrogen present on these two planets is very large (Table 4-3), even when allowance is made for H_2O frozen in the polar caps of Mars (Fig. 4-11). Either

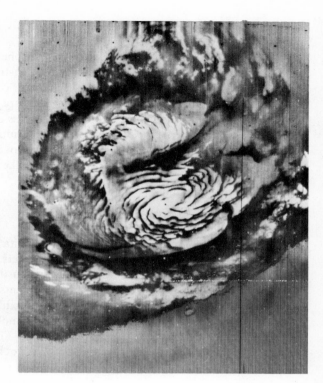

FIG. 4-11 Mariner 9's view of the north polar region of Mars; width of the field of view is 1,500 km. The season is summer for the Martian northern hemisphere, and the polar cap (the banded region, about 500 km wide) has shrunk to its minimum size. It consists of a layer of H_2O ice of uncertain thickness. The banding reflects underlying topography: on sunward-facing slopes or scarps ice has evaporated, exposing bands of darker rock or soil. In Martian winter, CO_2 frost covers a much larger area ($\sim 2,700$ km in diameter) at the pole. NASA photograph.

(1) Mars was endowed with smaller amounts of these elements from the outset, (2) degassing from the body of the planet to the atmosphere has been much less extensive on Mars than on Earth, (3) large amounts of volatile substances are hidden somewhere on Mars (e.g., frozen in the pores of the Martian soil or adsorbed on the surfaces of soil grains), or (4) there have been extensive, across-the-board losses from the Martian atmosphere.

Possibility (1) is least favored, because our understanding of the mode of origin of the planets (Chapter 7) indicates that the proportion of carbon, hydrogen, and nitrogen compounds incorporated by the accreting planets probably increased with distance outward from the sun. Thus Mars should have received more, rather than less, of these elements than Venus and Earth. Incomplete degassing (possibility 2) is indicated by Mars's low abundance of ^{36}Ar compared to Earth; this noble gas should have been driven out of both planets by heat, along with the other atmospheric gases, and should not have been subsequently lost by exospheric escape or by reaction with surface rocks or soil. The fact that Mars's atmosphere contains only ~ 3 percent as much ^{36}Ar per square centimeter of surface area as Earth's atmosphere suggests that a large fraction of Mars's potential atmospheric gases has not yet been liberated from the interior of the planet.

The presence of large amounts of permafrost ice in the Martian soil (possibility 3) is strongly suggested by the astrogeologic evidence of stream erosion by liquid water at various times in the past (Chapter 3). Extensive losses of at least one gas, nitrogen, from the exosphere (possibility 4) have been postulated to account for the observation by instruments in the Viking spacecraft that the Martian nitrogen contains a larger component of the isotope ^{15}N than does terrestrial nitrogen. Exospheric escape is somewhat easier for the isotope ^{14}N than it is for ^{15}N, and large-scale loss of gases to space would result in an enrichment of the heavy isotope in the residual planetary atmosphere.

The reader is referred to the Foundations of Earth Sciences Series volume *Atmospheres* by R.M. Goody and J.C.G. Walker, where these processes are discussed in the detail they deserve.

JOVIAN PLANETS AND SATELLITES

From Jupiter outward the planets are qualitatively different from the inner or terrestrial planets. The outer, or Jovian, planets are much more massive than the terrestrial planets, yet have smaller mean densities (Table 4-1). Clearly, their compositions are dominated by the lighter elements of the periodic table (H, He, C, N, O), rather than by the metals and metal oxides that the terrestrial planets are made of. The spectroscopically identifiable molecules in the atmospheres of the Jovian planets are H_2 and H compounds (Table 4-4). Hydrogen in the atmospheres of these massive, cold planets has not been significantly depleted by exospheric escape.

Table 4-4 Chemistry of Jovian Planets and the Sun

	Compounds Observed in Atmospheres	INFERRED OVERALL COMPOSITIONS OF PLANETS (wt. pct. of major constituents)[a]		
		H_2, He (gas)	H_2O, CH_4, NH_3 ("ice")	SiO_2, MgO, Fe ("earth")
JUPITER	H_2, He, CH_4, NH_3	82	5	13
SATURN	H_2, CH_4, (NH_3)	67	12	21
URANUS	H_2, CH_4	15	60	25
NEPTUNE	H_2, CH_4	10	70	20
SUN	—	98.5	1.2	0.3

[a]After M. Podolak and A. G. W. Cameron, Icarus, v. 22, 1974, 123–148.

The compositions and internal structures of the Jovian planets are investigated by a process of modeling and attempting to satisfy constraints (e.g., mean densities and moment-of-inertia factors; Table 4-1), much as was discussed earlier for the case of the terrestrial planets. The difference is that the properties of normally gaseous, rather than earthy, materials must be considered under conditions of high pressure and temperature.

Jupiter

In the case of Jupiter, the problem centers around the behavior of hydrogen gas over an extremely wide range of pressures. Modeling indicates that the low density of this planet cannot be accounted for unless hydrogen, the lightest of all elements, is the dominant component. Down to a depth of $\sim 25,000$ km, Jupiter consists largely of molecular H_2 gas, in a state similar to the gases in planetary atmospheres discussed previously, although very highly compressed at depth. Because of the great pressure, the hydrogen beneath $\sim 25,000$ km is believed to exist in a different physical state, that of metallic hydrogen (which nonetheless behaves as a fluid). The gas is "metallic" in the sense that electrons have become detached from the nuclei of gas atoms and are free to move about through the compressed medium. This is also a fundamental property of the metals that we are more familiar with, and gives rise to their high electrical and thermal conductivity.

In detail, Jupiter models also contain some He, H_2O, CH_4, NH_3, and other gases, which are more or less uniformly mixed through the hydrogen, and earthy substances (SiO_2, MgO, Fe) that are concentrated as a core at the center of the planet (Fig. 4-12). The models that most accurately account for Jupiter's properties contain these secondary components in proportions that are larger than their abundances in undifferentiated solar material (Table 4-4), but the

FIG. 4-12 Models of the interiors of the Jovian planets; Earth is shown for scale. Four major compositional components are shown. The first two include helium and other gaseous species as well as hydrogen. "Ices" are H_2O, CH_4, and NH_3, which can exist as solids even at high temperatures, if the pressure is high enough. Solid "ice" is shown in three of the models, but this may or may not be present, depending on internal temperatures of these planets. After M. Podolak and A. G. W. Cameron, *Icarus*, v. 22, 1974, 123–148.

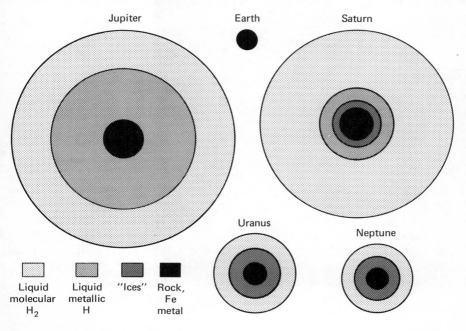

Jupiter   Earth   Saturn

Uranus   Neptune

| Liquid molecular H_2 | Liquid metallic H | "Ices" | Rock, Fe metal |

differences are not very great; it is not misleading to think of Jupiter as a "small sun" that never caught fire. These models also postulate an earthy core at the center of Jupiter that may amount to 10 times the mass of Earth; it is believed to experience 30,000°K of temperature and 300 million atmospheres (atm) of pressure.

Thermal models of Jupiter's interior are based on observations that the planet emits about twice as much energy as it receives from the sun; there is an internal energy source. This seems most likely to be heat that was generated by events surrounding the origin of Jupiter (Chapter 7), which is still diffusing out of the interior of the planet and being dissipated into space. The outward flow of heat keeps Jupiter's interior zone of metallic hydrogen in convective motion, and movements of this conductive material are held responsible for the mighty magnetic field that surrounds the planet (the dynamo theory). Electrons and protons, trapped from the solar wind by the magnetic field, form radiation belts about Jupiter similar to those that surround Earth.

The visible surface of Jupiter (Fig. 4-13) consists of clouds arrayed in parallel *zones* (light in color) and *belts* (darker). The atmosphere is in convective motion; zones are regions of relatively warm, rising gas, which descends in the adjacent belts after it cools. The visible clouds are believed to consist of crystals of solid ammonia—"snowflakes"—suspended in the atmosphere of hydrogen and helium described previously. From our model of the composition of Jupiter and the run of temperature and pressure in it, we can calculate which compounds ought to condense as crystals or liquids in the outermost regions of the planet

FIG. 4-13 Jupiter, photographed by Pioneer 10 in 1973. Zones (light) and belts (darker) of clouds cover the surface. The Great Red Spot (left), which has been visible for at least three centuries, is believed to be a meteorological phenomenon akin to a hurricane on Earth. Dark spot at right is the shadow of Io, a satellite of Jupiter. NASA photograph.

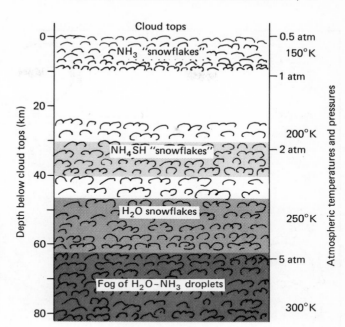

FIG. 4-14 Model of the outer cloud layers in Jupiter's atmosphere, based on considerations of chemical stability. Snowflakes and water droplets are suspended in an atmosphere of H_2 and He. NH_4SH is ammonium hydrosulfide. After J. S. Lewis, *Icarus*, v. 10, 1969, 365–378.

(Fig. 4-14); this figure does not represent observations, of course, but a model based on a model.

Jupiter's clouds are colored in delicate tints of red, brown, and blue. This coloration is believed to be due to the presence of small amounts of sulfur, red phosphorus, and/or complex organic molecules.

Saturn, Uranus, Neptune

Models have also been derived for these planets, but with progressively less confidence than attaches to the Jupiter model, because less is known about them that can be used to constrain the range of possible models. The Jovian planet models (Table 4-4, Fig. 4-12) taken together appear to display a trend, in that the farther a planet is from the sun, the smaller its content of hydrogen and helium is, and the larger is its component of denser "ices." This is required to account for the relatively high densities of the outer Jovian planets. The probable significance of this trend is discussed in Chapter 7.

Pluto

Very little is known about the farthest, coldest planet discovered in the solar system. Its mass and therefore its density are essentially unknown. It is probably a solid body, without an atmosphere; H_2 and He may well have escaped an object as small as Pluto (about the size of Earth's moon); other species would have frozen out. The spectrum of frozen methane, which condenses at 50°K and less, has been observed on Pluto.

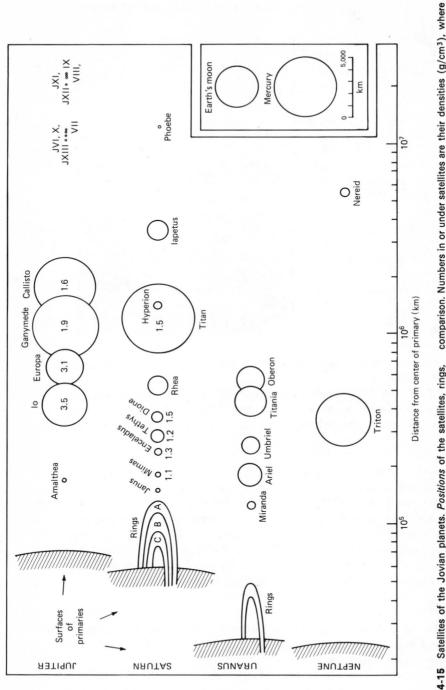

FIG. 4-15 Satellites of the Jovian planets. *Positions* of the satellites, rings, and planetary surfaces are indicated by the logarithmic scale beneath the diagram. *Sizes* of the satellites, greatly exaggerated of course, are relative to the linear scale at lower right. Sizes of Mercury and Earth's moon are shown for comparison. Numbers in or under satellites are their densities (g/cm^3), where these can be estimated. Diameters and densities are highly uncertain except for those of Io, Europa, Ganymede, Callisto, and Titan.

Pluto may represent the ultimate end member of the progression of planet compositions mentioned above (i.e., all ice and earth, no H_2 or He). Most of the generalizations made earlier about Jovian planets, which relate to their low density and hydrogen-rich compositions, probably do not extend to Pluto.

Satellites of the Jovian Planets

All the outer planets except Pluto are circled by two or more satellites (Fig. 4-15). These should not be considered insignificant members of the solar system; four of them are comparable in dimension to the planet Mercury. Their apparent densities range from that of rock (Io, ~ 3.5 g/cm^3) to values appropriate to ice (Mimas and Tethys, ~ 1.2 g/cm^3).

Studies of the reflection spectra and other photometric properties of the brighter Jovian satellites tell us something about the compositions of their surfaces. Europa and Ganymede are covered with H_2O ice or frost, and the surface of Callisto appears to consist of rock or earthy dust. The small inner satellites of Saturn are probably frost covered.

Io's surface is light in color, yet lacks the spectral features of H_2O ice. The spectrum of Io suggests instead that the satellite is covered with evaporite deposits, concentrations of salts of Mg, Na, SO_4, and other ions that may have been leached from Io's interior in watery solutions, which percolated to the satellite's surface where the H_2O evaporated.

Titan is the only Jovian satellite known to have a substantial atmosphere (at least 0.1 atm pressure). The lines of CH_4 and H_2 have been observed in its spectrum, although H_2 must escape very rapidly from Titan. There are clouds of unknown composition in the atmosphere.

Interior modeling indicates that the Jovian satellites range in character from totally rocky (Io), through rock largely overlain by ice (Europa, Ganymede) or by an ocean of liquid water and a floating layer of ice (Callisto), to balls of pure ice or snow (the small inner satellites of Saturn). Titan's interior may be similar to Ganymede's, but with an added component of NH_3 and CH_4 hydrates.

Most of the Jovian satellites move in extremely regular orbits with very small eccentricities and inclinations to the equators of their primaries. The satellites with orbital mean distances greater than 3×10^6 km, however, have substantial eccentricities and inclinations. The outermost group of four small Jupiter satellites, as well as Phoebe and Triton, are actually in retrograde rotation. The eight small outer satellites of Jupiter are probably captured asteroids; the inner larger satellites are thought to have accreted in orbit around Jupiter, in a situation that imposed the same direction of rotation on the planet and its satellites (Chapter 7). Objects can be captured into retrograde orbits about as readily as direct orbits.

The rings of Saturn (Fig. 4-16) consist of vast swarms of H_2O ice chunks, each a few centimeters in dimension, moving in orbits of such small inclination that the chunks are never more than ~ 1 km out of the equatorial plane of the

FIG. 4-16 Saturn, with its prominent rings of orbiting ice particles. Zones and belts similar to those on Jupiter can be seen on the surface of the planet. Photograph courtesy of S. M. Larson, Lunar and Planetary Laboratory, University of Arizona.

planet. Why is this ice spread out in rings, instead of being collected into one or more satellites inside the orbit of Janus? Planets exert tidal stresses on their satellites (Fig. 2-9), and the closer a satellite is to its planet, the greater is the tidal stress. Self-gravitation tends to hold the satellite together, but there is a critical distance between planet and satellite inside of which the tidal stresses are simply too great to be opposed: an object that moves inside this *Roche limit* is disrupted. Conversely, dispersed matter orbiting inside a planet's Roche limit cannot accrete into a satellite. The Roche limit (*d*) for a satellite larger than ∼1,000 km in diameter,* of density ρ, is

$$d = \sqrt[3]{\frac{6M}{\pi\rho}} \tag{4-2}$$

where *M* is the mass of the primary planet. The rings of Saturn lie inside the planet's Roche limit; the satellite Janus orbits safely outside it.

---

*This size limit is imposed because the physical strength of an object smaller than ∼1,000 km, as well as its self-gravitation, acts to resist tidal stresses and hold the object together; Eq. (4-2) does not take account of physical strength. Larger objects also have physical strength, but gravitational and tidal forces are so much greater than physical strength that it can be neglected, and the Roche limit can be calculated simply on the basis of the competition between tides and self-gravitation.

five

rocks from space:
meteorites
and lunar samples

The view of the solar system laid out in the first four chapters is based on remote measurements, made with Earth-based telescopes and ingeniously designed spacecraft that orbit or land on other planets. The amount that can be learned by these means is very great. A whole new perspective opens up, however, when samples of other planets can actually be brought back to Earth and studied in detail. So far this has been possible for only two classes of material: meteorites (which come to us of their own free will), and lunar samples (collected by the exertions of the U.S. and Soviet space programs). Meteorites and lunar samples have been studied intensively; space permits only the briefest summary of this body of knowledge. *Cosmochemistry* is the name most often applied to this field of endeavor.

Meteorites and lunar samples are treated separately below. Much of the interpretive discussion that attaches to meteorites, and some additional descriptive material, appears in Chapter 7.

METEORITES

Interplanetary space contains a certain amount of stony rubble derived from collisions between asteriods and the wasting away of comets. Fragments of debris (*meteoroids*) move in elliptical orbits and tend to be swept up by Earth and the other planets. Encounter velocities of these objects with Earth are 11 to 30 km/sec. Their fate upon plunging into the terrestrial atmosphere depends upon their size (Table 5-1). All are heated to incandescence by atmospheric friction, and ablation of melted surface material leaves a fiery trail in the sky.

Table 5-1 Capture of Interplanetary Debris by Earth

Log Mass of Meteoroid	Nature of Interaction with Earth	Name Applied to Atmospheric Phenomenon	Very Approx. Rate of Capture by Earth, Per Year
·	(Short-lived and rare in solar system; blown away by light pressure)		
·			
·			
−12			
−11	Decelerated in upper atmosphere without melting		
−10			
−9			
−8			
−7			
−6 (microgram)	Ablation-melted in upper atmosphere, dispersed in microscopic spherules; much vaporized		
−5			
−4			
−3 (milligram)			·
−2		Meteor	·
−1			·
0 (gram)			
1	Decelerated by drag in lower atmosphere; partly ablated, but interior reaches Earth's surface intact	Fireball	1,000,000,000
2			100,000,000
3 (kilogram)			10,000,000
4			1,000,000
5			100,000
6 (ton)			10,000
7			1,000
8			100
9	Iron meteorites unchecked by atmospheric drag; impact surface of Earth at 11 to 30 km/sec, excavate crater; stones fragment in atmosphere, decelerate as above	Bolide (sonic booms)	1
10			0.1
11			0.01
·			·
·			·
·			·

Ablation completely destroys the smaller meteoroids, but interior portions of objects larger than a few grams in mass survive. Having been decelerated by atmospheric drag to a few hundred meters per second, they fall intact to Earth. Once it has fallen to Earth, a meteoroid is properly termed a *meteorite*.

FIG. 5-1 Exterior surface of the Lafayette (Indiana) stony meteorite, showing a well-developed flight form and fusion crust. Ridges of melted rock that flowed back from the leading edge of the ablating meteorite (center of exposed face) are still preserved. Diameter of the stone, about 10 cm. Figure courtesy of Field Museum of Natural History.

Meteorites usually display fusion crusts (Fig. 5-1), relicts of their ablative passage through the atmosphere. There is evidence of thermal damage in a zone a few millimeters thick beneath the fusion crust, but apart from this the interiors of meteorites are unaffected by the high-temperature ablation of their surfaces.

The column of air a meteoroid must displace as it falls to Earth varies as the square of its dimension (i.e., as its cross-sectional area), while the mass of the meteoroid varies as the cube of its dimension. Meteoroids larger than a certain size (~ 100 tons, several meters in diameter) are more massive than the column of air that they must displace, so the atmosphere is incapable of decelerating them substantially. Pressure of the air against the face of incoming large stone meteorites tends to break them up, however, after which the small fragments are quickly decelerated. Large iron meteorites (fortunately very rare) are more likely to hang together and impact the ground at velocities of tens of kilometers per second, excavating explosion craters (Chapter 3). Fragments of iron meteorites, often severely shock damaged, can sometimes be found in and around terrestrial impact craters.

Some 10 or 20 new meteorites are recovered each year and added to the collections of the natural history museums of the world. Each meteorite is given the geographical name of its point of recovery. There are about 3,000 meteorites preserved in collections. Roughly 1,000 were actually seen to fall from the sky and recovered (*falls*); the others have simply been found and recognized to be meteorites (*finds*).

When these missiles from space are examined, five major types of material are discovered (Fig. 5-2). These are discussed below. Each meteorite type can be further divided into a number of discrete subtypes, but most of these will not be explicitly described in this book.

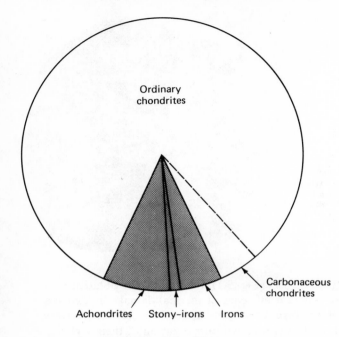

FIG. 5-2 Proportions of major types among meteorites observed to fall to Earth (falls). The enstatite chondrite subtype is included with "ordinary chondrites."

Carbonaceous Chondrites

Carbonaceous chondrites are gray to black in color and consist of agglomerations of two principal components: hard bits of mineral matter, each 1 or 2 mm in dimension; and a matrix of very fine grained, blackish earthy material in which the hard bits are studded, like plums in a pudding (Fig. 5-3). The proportion of hard bits varies from zero to over 50 percent among the carbonaceous chondrite subtypes.

Microscopic examination shows the "hard bits" to be miniature igneous rocks composed of high-temperature, anhydrous minerals. Two categories of "bits" should be distinguished. *Chondrules* (Fig. 5-4(A)) are rounded or subrounded in form. Clearly, some were once droplets of molten rocky material that solidified while in a dispersed state; all chondrules may have had this origin. Most consist of olivine and orthopyroxene in varying proportions. Minor amounts of pigeonitic pyroxene, nickel–iron metal, troilite (FeS), and residual glass are also present in many cases. The coexistence of metallic iron with (generally, magnesium-rich) olivine and pyroxene in many of the chondrules reflects an oxygen-poor environment of formation (i.e., a *reducing* environment). If the chondrules had been melted in an oxidizing environment, their metallic iron would have been oxidixed to FeO, which would have entered the olivine and pyroxene that crystallized upon cooling.

The other, less-abundant type of "hard bit" in carbonaceous chondrites also consists of high-temperature anhydrous minerals, but these "bits" are irregular in form (Figure 5-4(B)), and it is not clear that most of them ever

FIG. 5-3 (Right) Fragment of the Allende (Mexico) carbonaceous chondrite. The upper surface is covered with fusion crust; abundant Ca,Al-rich inclusions (I) and rounded chondrules (C) are exposed on fracture surfaces. Smithsonian Astrophysical Observatory photograph.

0   cm   1

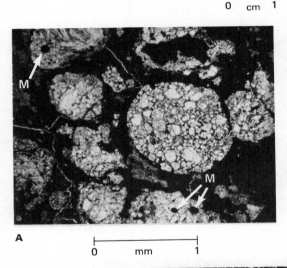

A

0   mm   1

FIG. 5-4 Photomicrographs of chondrules and a high-temperature inclusion in thin sections of carbonaceous chondrites. The matrix in which chondrules and inclusions are embedded appears black. (A) Chondrules, composed chiefly of magnesian olivine and pyroxene, in the Renazzo meteorite. These enclose a few grains of nickel–iron metal (M). (B) A high-temperature inclusion in the Vigarano chondrite. Fine-grained minerals present are melilite, spinel, and other Ca,Al-rich refractory compounds. Smithsonian Astrophysical Observatory photographs.

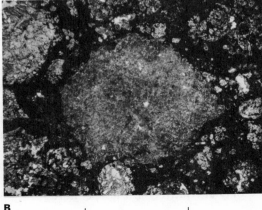

B

0   mm   1

passed through a molten stage. They may be aggregations of minerals that formed by some other high-temperature process (specifically, it has been proposed that they condensed as solids from a cooling vapor; Chapter 7). Their mineralogy also differs from that of the chondrules. In addition to common meteoritic minerals such as olivine and diopside, they contain or consist largely of uncommon minerals: spinel ($MgAl_2O_4$), fassaite (Al, Ti-rich pyroxene), melilite ($Ca_2Al_2SiO_7$–$Ca_2MgSi_2O_7$), grossular ($Ca_3Al_2(SiO_4)_3$), perovskite ($CaTiO_3$), and others. What these minerals have in common is their enrichment in calcium, aluminum, magnesium, and titanium relative to silicon. These are comparatively refractory elements, in the sense that they would be the first to condense from a cooling vapor of solar composition (Chapter 7). "Hard bits" of the second type are usually referred to as Ca,Al-rich *inclusions*, to set them apart from chondrules.

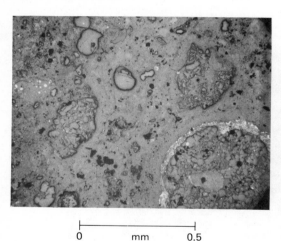

FIG. 5-5 A polished section of the Pollen carbonaceous chondrite, viewed by reflected light. Chondrules and mineral grains are seen to be embedded in a fine-grained, nondescript matrix (gray; black spots are pits or voids in the section surface). The matrix is opaque and appears black by transmitted light (Fig. 5-4). It consists of low-temperature minerals, chiefly phyllosilicates. Smithsonian Astrophysical Observatory photograph.

The fine-grained matrix of most carbonaceous chondrites, in which chondrules and high-temperature inclusions are embedded (Fig. 5-5), consists mostly of ill-defined phyllosilicate minerals: hydrated sheet-structure silicate compounds similar to the terrestrial minerals serpentine or montmorillonite. Magnetite (Fe_3O_4), Fe,Ni-sulfide, and the carbonates and sulfates of calcium and magnesium are present in lesser amounts. All these are low-temperature minerals, in contrast to the substance of the chondrules and Ca,Al-rich inclusions: clearly, these two components of carbonaceous chondrites were formed under very different circumstances, then brought together.

One other important matrix constituent is present. Carbonaceous chondrites take their name from the fact that their matrices are impregnated with a tarry mixture of complex organic compounds in amounts up to 5 percent by weight. Like the other matrix constituents, these organic compounds are stable only at relatively low temperatures.

Ordinary Chondrites

Ordinary chondrites fall to Earth in greater numbers than any other meteorite type (Fig. 5-2). They tend to be harder, lighter in color, and more obviously crystalline in nature than carbonaceous chondrites. They have essentially the same chemical composition as carbonaceous chondrites, as far as the proportions of major metallic elements are concerned; but they are devoid of water and organic compounds, and substantially depleted in their levels of volatile trace elements (i.e., elements that would condense from the vapor state at relatively low temperatures; Fig. 5-6). The ordinary chondrites consist entirely of high-temperature minerals: olivine, orthopyroxene, alloys of nickel–iron metal, troilite, and minor amounts of sodic plagioclase, diopside, and chromite. The minerals in most ordinary chondrites tend to be remarkably uniform in composition; taken together, they represent very nearly the equilibrium mineral assemblage that would be expected to develop in a rock of chondritic composition if it was held at moderately high temperatures (500–1,000°C) in a closed system. (This is in contrast to the situation in carbonaceous chondrites, where the mixture of high- and low-temperature minerals, many having variable compositions, is grossly out of equilibrium.)

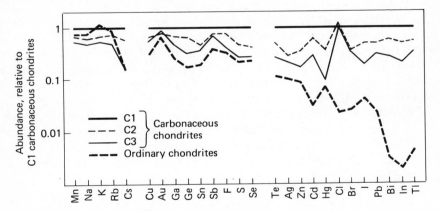

FIG. 5-6 Volatile elements, which are present in C1 carbonaceous chondrites in approximately the same proportions as in the sun (Fig. 5-8), are depleted to varying degrees in other types of chondritic meteorites. (The C1, C2, and C3 subtypes of carbonaceous chondrites contain progressively smaller amounts of carbon, water, and volatile trace elements, as shown, and larger proportions of chondrules and Ca,Al-rich inclusions.) After J. W. Larimer and E. Anders, 1967, *Geochim. Cosmochim. Acta*, v. 31, 1239–1270.

Ordinary chondrites consist of chondrules embedded in matrix, much like carbonaceous chondrites, but in this case the matrices tend to have the same mineralogy as the chondrules, and the boundaries between chondrules and matrix are often indistinct (Fig. 5-7). The textures of most of them resemble those of granulitic metamorphic rocks; thermal metamorphism has coarsened their textures and softened the distinction between chondrules and matrix. Metamorphism also has the potential of moving ions from one mineral to

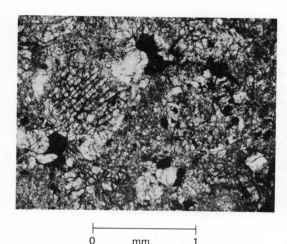

FIG. 5-7 An intensely metamorphosed chondrite, the Colby (Wisconsin) meteorite, viewed in thin section by transmitted light. This consists almost entirely of coarse olivine and pyroxene (light) and metal and troilite (black). Several chondrules are visible, but their boundaries have been blurred by metamorphism. Smithsonian Astrophysical Observatory photograph.

```
|————————————————————|
0        mm         1
```

another by solid-state diffusion. This probably accounts for the ordinary chondrites' present state of uniform, equilibrium mineralogy; if they were previously untidy, disequilibrium assemblages like the carbonaceous chondrites, metamorphism would have had the effect of dismantling the out-of-equilibrium minerals and moving the ions that they had been made of to places where they could be used to form new, uniform, equilibrium minerals. This could be why we see no relics of Ca,Al-rich inclusions in ordinary chondrites; the exotic minerals in them were grossly out of equilibrium with other more abundant chondritic minerals, so metamorphism would have systematically obliterated them.

It is unclear whether metamorphism also drove water, carbon compounds, and volatile trace elements out of materials that was initially similar to carbonaceous chondrite material, or whether metamorphism occurred in a closed system, acting on material that had been depleted in these volatile components from the outset.

Chondrites as Primitive Planetary Material

The chemical composition of C1* carbonaceous chondrites has a special significance: it is very similar to the composition of the sun, at least as far as the abundances of condensable elements are concerned (Fig. 5-8). Thus, if a mass of gas were extracted from the sun and cooled to $\sim 200°K$, and if all the elements capable of condensing at that temperature (this excludes most hydrogen, carbon, nitrogen and noble gases) were accumulated, the condensate would be chemically similar to the carbonaceous chondrites. This suggests that chondrites are samples

*See the caption to Fig. 5-6.

of planetary material that formed at the same time the sun did, and that they have never since experienced bulk melting and igneous fractionation.

The primitive character of chondritic meteorites is also indicated by their radiometric ages, often about 4.6×10^9 years, which are the oldest of any known type of planetary material (Fig. 5-24). But does "oldest known" necessarily mean that the chondrites go back to the very beginning? Might not the solar system have had a long and complicated history prior to the time when the chondrites were formed and their radiometric clocks set? Apparently not. Evidence to the contrary comes from the observation of anomalies in the isotopic compositions of certain elements in chondrites. These anomalies are attributable to the decay in their present sites of several very-short-lived radioactive nuclides, such as ^{129}I (half-life of 16×10^6 yr), ^{244}Pu (82×10^6 yr), and ^{26}Al (10^6 yr), that were once present in the chondrites. These nuclides were produced by violent events in stars elsewhere in the galaxy (Chapter 6), then dispersed, captured in the infant solar system, and incorporated in chondritic planetary material, all before they (the nuclides) had time to decay away to insignificant levels—that is, in no more than a few half-lives of the shortest-

FIG. 5-8 Comparison of abundances of condensible elements in C1 carbonaceous chondrites with abundances in the sun. In both cases abundances are in terms of atoms per silicon atom. Figure courtesy of H. Holweger.

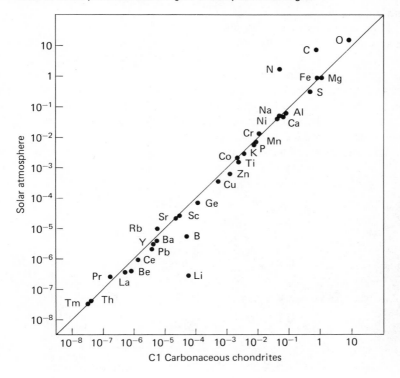

lived nuclide, ^{26}Al. Thereafter, the products of their decay accumulated in the chondrites, registering the isotopic anomalies we observe today. If a substantial span of time had separated the origin of the solar system and the formation of the chondrites, no short-lived radioactive nuclides would have been left to be incorporated in the latter, and the isotopic anomalies mentioned above would not be observed. Therefore, chondrites are generally held to have been formed when the solar system did, and their maximum apparent age, 4.6×10^9 yr, is understood to be the age of the solar system.

Processes that operated when the solar system was being formed were responsible for the peculiar properties of the chondrites—the chondrules and the high-temperature inclusions, and the disequilibrium mixture of high- and low-temperature minerals that they are composed of. We gain valuable insights into the origin of the solar system from consideration of these properties of meteorites, which are discussed in Chapter 7.

Achondrites

Achondrites and chondrites together comprise the broad category of *stony meteorites*. Chondrites are quite dissimilar to any kind of terrestrial rock, however, whereas most achondrites are very much like terrestrial igneous rocks. Specifically, they consist of ultramafic and gabbroic plutonic rocks and basaltic volcanic rocks.

Most achondrites can be placed in the subtype of *Ca-rich achondrites*; these appear to be genetically related, and are of particular interest because they are broadly similar to many of the samples from the moon, implying that they came from a place in the solar system where geologic processes once operated much as they did in the moon. The possibility that they actually came from the moon can be eliminated, however, now that we have authentic lunar samples for comparison. The second most abundant achondrite subtype, *aubrites*, consists of extremely magnesian (En_{99}) pyroxenites.

The preceding discussion is in terms of massive, crystalline, igneous rocks.

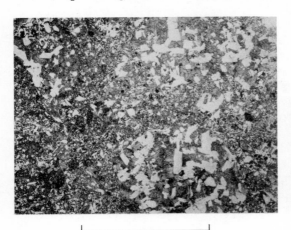

FIG. 5-9 Photomicrograph by transmitted light of the Stannern (Czechoslovakia) meteorite, a Ca-rich achondrite. Visible are plagioclase (white) and clinopyroxenes (gray) in textures characteristic of terrestrial volcanic basalts. The rock is a breccia, in which fragments of coarse- and fine-grained basalts are mingled. Smithsonian Astrophysical Observatory photograph.

0   cm   1

In fact, most achondrites (and many chondrites, for that matter) are *breccias*, aggregations of rock and mineral fragments (Fig. 5-9) that have been broken up by violent events of some kind, probably hypervelocity impacts in space. Some meteorites contain fragments (*clasts*) of several different rock types mixed together.

Irons

Iron meteorites consist largely of massive nickel–iron metal, generally with a nickel content of 5 to 10 percent. Minor minerals are troilite, schreibersite $((Fe,Ni)_3P)$, and cohenite (Fe_3C). Iron meteorites are rarely breccias, in contrast to stony meteorites, probably because of their superior strength.

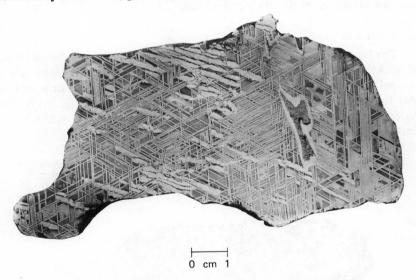

0 cm 1

FIG. 5-10 Polished and etched slab of the Edmonton (Kentucky) octahedrite, illustrating the Widmanstätten structure. Narrow parallel bands are cross sections of plates of the low-nickel alloy kamacite; the spaces between them are filled with higher-nickel alloys. Smithsonian Astrophysical Observatory photograph.

The most abundant iron meteorite subtype, the *octahedrites*, consists of two discrete metallic alloys arranged in a characteristic geometry (the *Widmanstätten structure*), which is visible on polished and chemically etched surfaces (Fig. 5-10). This structure developed during slow cooling of the octahedrites from high temperatures: the kamacite plates (low-nickel alloy) nucleated in what were originally huge crystals of pure taenite (high-nickel alloy), then grew in thickness, and the nickel contents of both the kamacite and the taenite alloys changed as they adapted to new equilibrium conditions at lower temperatures. Solid-state diffusion of nickel and iron atoms through the crystals was the mechanism that made this separation into two alloys possible.

The compositions and compositional heterogeneities of alloys in the

Widmanstätten structure are of particular interest because the equilibrium compositions and diffusion rates in nickel–iron alloys, as a function of temperature, are known with considerable accuracy from laboratory studies. This makes it possible to deduce the history of declining temperatures that the octahedrites must have experienced to establish the pattern of compositions and compositional gradients that we observe in them. It turns out that the octahedrites cooled through the temperature range of 600 to 400°C very slowly, at rates of only a few degrees Celsius in each million years.

The same type of analysis can be applied to the grains of nickel–iron metal that occur scattered among the silicate minerals of ordinary chondrites. We find that these stony meteorites cooled from metamorphic temperatures at about the same rate as did the octahedrites.

Stony Irons

The least abundant meteorite type, stony irons, consists of silicate minerals and nickel–iron metal in approximately equal proportions. There are two principal subtypes. *Pallasites* consist of coarse olivine crystals in a matrix of metal that displays an interrupted Widmanstätten pattern (Fig. 5-11). *Mesosiderites* are brecciated and metamorphosed mixtures of Ca-rich achondrite silicate minerals, with metal.

FIG. 5-11 Polished slab of a pallasitic (stony-iron) portion of the Brenham (Kansas) meteorite. Coarse, rounded crystals of olivine are embedded in massive nickel–iron metal (white by reflected light). Photograph courtesy of the American Museum of Natural History.

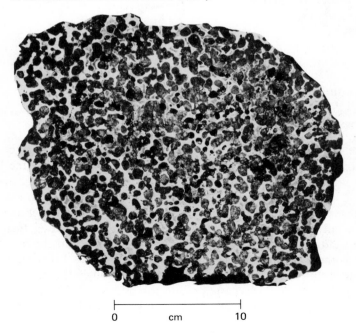

```
|————————————————————————|
0          cm            10
```

Compositional gradients in the metal alloys of pallasites and mesosiderites indicate that both cooled even more slowly than the octahedrites did.

Parent Meteorite Planets

The slow rate of cooling registered by metal alloys in most of the meteorites, and the fact that some of them (achondrites) are the products of igneous fractionation (which requires a gravitational field to separate liquids from crystals), indicates that the meteorites once resided in one or more planets. These properties could not have developed if meteorites had always been small objects orbiting at large in the solar system. The interiors of these bodies must have become hot, just as Earth's interior is; this had the effect of metamorphosing some primitive planetary material (producing ordinary chondrites) and causing melting elsewhere. Components of the melted material separated gravitationally, yielding zones of pure metal (the source of iron meteorites) and pure silicates (achondrites).

The rate at which a rock cools depends upon how deeply it is buried: the less overburden, the faster it dissipates heat to space. The cooling rates found for octahedrites and ordinary chondrites correspond to depths of 100 to 200 km in a small planet. The parent meteorite planets were probably not much larger than a few hundred kilometers in radius, that is, of asteroidal dimensions. Origin in smallish planets is further indicated by the absence of high-pressure minerals* (other than those attributable to impact effects) in meteorites. These would have developed if meteorites had once resided deep inside planets of greater-than-asteroidal dimensions.

The amount of chemical diversity among meteorite types makes it difficult to postulate that they were once related in a single planet that was somehow disrupted. In addition, there are differences in the isotopic composition of oxygen in the various types that cannot be understood if all were derived from a common geochemical system. It is much easier to understand the properties of meteorites if they came from a number of discrete parent bodies.

The source of the heat that affected the small meteorite parent planets is something of a puzzle. The heating was drastic but ended quickly, allowing the meteorite planets to cool off in time to register the ^{129}I and ^{244}Pu isotopic anomalies noted above.† Uranium, thorium, and ^{40}K decay too slowly to be a suitable heat source, and not enough energy is deposited during the accretion of planets as small as asteriods to raise their temperature importantly. The most likely sources of early heating are the decay of short-lived ^{26}Al (we know some

---

*Such as pyrope garnet, $Mg_3Al_2(SiO_4)_3$, and jadeitic pyroxene, $NaAl(SiO_3)_2$, minerals that occur in terrestrial rocks of deep origin.

†Only anomalies due to these two nuclides have been observed in the same meteorites that have been severely heated. Isotopic anomalies attributable to the very short half-life nuclide ^{26}Al are displayed by Allende, a meteorite that has not been strongly heated.

was present, from the isotopic anomalies just mentioned, but was there enough to do the job?), or the heating effect of electrical currents induced in the planets by plasma motions in the early solar system (referred to in Chapters 4 and 7).

Asteroids as Parent Planets

If internal evidence indicates that the meteorites came from multiple asteroid-sized bodies, are we not compelled to conclude that the parent bodies were, in fact, asteroids? The atmospheric entry trajectories and velocities of three meteorites have been determined precisely enough (by being photographed by multiple-station meteor cameras) to permit calculation of their preterrestrial orbits in space (Fig. 5-12), and these closely resemble the orbits of known asteroids that cross Earth's orbit or reach perihelion near it (Apollo or Amor asteroids, respectively).

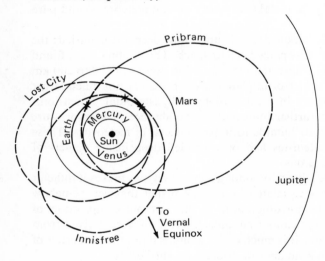

FIG. 5-12 Preterrestrial orbits of three chondritic meteorites (Príbram, Lost City, Innisfree) whose flight through the atmosphere was precisely documented by meteor cameras. After I. Halliday, *Sky and Telescope*, v. 53, 1977, 339.

The technique of remote multispectral photometry (described in Chapter 3) has been turned on 98 individual asteroids, and some striking correspondences have been found between the asteroid spectra and the spectra measured for meteorite powders in the laboratory (Fig. 5-13). The proportions of "meteorite types" found among the asteroids are very different than among meteorites that fall to Earth, however. The most abundant meteorite type on Earth, ordinary chondrites, is represented by only five asteroids; but three of these (such as 887 Alinda) are in orbits that come close to Earth's, so their debris is especially likely to be swept up by Earth.

The spectra of most belt asteroids appear to correspond to carbonaceous chondrites and stony-iron meteorites (see 176 Iduna and 230 Amantis, Fig. 5-13), types that fall relatively rarely to Earth. There is a close correspondence between the spectra of Ca-rich achondrites and a single asteroid, 4 Vesta;

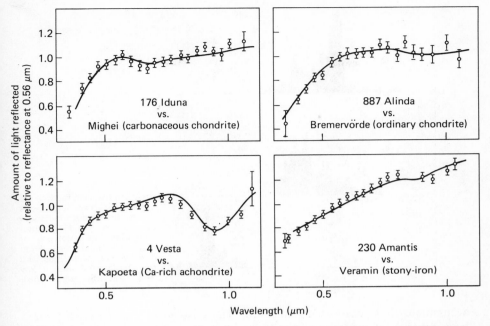

FIG. 5-13 Comparison of reflection spectra of four asteroids (points with error bars; measured with ground-based telescopes) with spectra of powdered samples of four meteorites (solid curves). After C. R. Chapman, *Geochim. Cosmochim. Acta*, v. 40, 1976, 701–719.

evidently, this small object (radius, 270 km) has had an igneous history similar to that of the moon.

Cosmic-Ray Exposure Ages of Meteorites

Asteroids tend to collide with one another with calculable frequency, and meteorite-sized fragments are broken loose and released in independent orbits. Over a period of time each fragment suffers additional knocks or collisions and is gravitationally perturbed by the planets, so that it takes up a succession of orbits, each with different orbital elements. In the end the fragment is either (1) pulverized by an especially high-momentum collision, (2) swept up by one of the planets, or (3) perturbed by passage close to a planet into an orbit that ejects it from the solar system altogether.

In the case of fragments that are captured by Earth (meteorites), we are able to determine the length of time that they spent as small objects in space by measuring their content of certain nuclides (such as ^3H, ^3He, ^{20}Ne, ^{21}Ne, ^{22}Ne, ^{36}Ar, ^{38}Ar) that are generated by the action of cosmic rays on rocky material. Prior to the time when they were broken out of their parent planets, they were shielded from cosmic radiation (which is largely absorbed by several meters of rock); only during their existence as small rocks in space did they

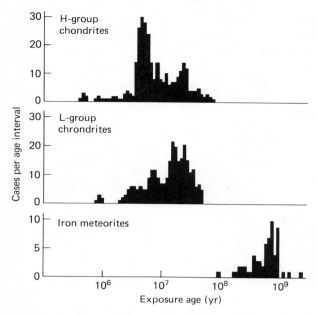

FIG. 5-14 Distribution of cosmic-ray exposure ages found in several meteorite classes. H- and L-group chondrites are subtypes of ordinary chondrites. From J. A. Wood, *Meteorites and the Origin of Planets* (New York: McGraw-Hill, 1968), 117 pp.

accumulate these cosmogenic nuclides. The cosmic-ray exposure ages for a large number of ordinary chondrites and irons are shown in Fig. 5-14. The substantially younger ages for ordinary chondrites are probably due to (1) their greater accessibility in near-Earth orbits, mentioned above, and (2) their greater weakness and vulnerability to catastrophic collisions, which means that on an average they spend a shorter time as meteorite-sized objects before being broken into smaller fragments, than irons do.

Evolution of Meteorite Orbits

It is possible to computer-model the odyssey of a meteorite in space from the time it is knocked from its parent planet into an orbit with some assumed set of orbital elements, through the vicissitudes of collision and perturbation, until it meets one of the fates listed above. If many hypothetical fragments are started in orbits similar to those of Apollo asteroids, their mean time before capture by Earth (for those fragments that meet this fate) is found to be comparable to the cosmic-ray exposure ages of ordinary chondrites. Although this seems to account for the origin of most meteorites, it raises a problem about the origin of the Apollo asteroids themselves. These objects must have similarly short lifetimes, so they must be constantly replenished somehow. It is not clear where new Apollo asteroids would come from; computer modeling indicates that the orbits of normal belt asteroids do not evolve rapidly enough into Apollo asteroid orbits to provide a plausible source, unless there is some important dynamical effect that has not been included in the modeling. It has been suggested that the Apollo asteroids are not closely related to the belt asteroids at all, but are the involatile residues of comet nuclei, after the ices have sublimed away. In this case the Apollo asteroid family is constantly being replenished from the cloud of comets outside the solar system (Chapter 2). However, there are difficulties with this concept; the high-temperature, metamorphic character of the ordinary chondrites described in this chapter does not fit well with the "dirty snowball" model of comet nuclei (Chapter 2).

The smaller objects (meteors) near the top of Table 5-1 are believed to be derived from comets rather than asteroids, for the most part. Their behavior during atmospheric entry is appropriate to that of weak low-density objects rather than hard rock fragments; they are systematically destroyed by ablation and never recovered on the ground. Many (the shower meteors) occur at specific times of the year, presumably when Earth passes through the orbital path of the comet that shed them. In several cases the dates of meteor showers can be correlated with times when Earth crosses the orbits of still-active comets. Meteor orbits are often near-parabolic, but never pronouncedly hyperbolic; hence these objects do not have an extra-solar-system origin.

LUNAR SAMPLES

The surface of the moon is covered almost everywhere with an unconsolidated layer of rock debris (the *regolith*, Fig. 5-15), pulverized by billions of years of bombardment by meteoroids. Large impacts penetrate the regolith and shatter more of the underlying bedrock; small impacts expend their energy scattering and redepositing the soil of the regolith. Impacts of all sizes cause some melting of the soil, producing glassy particles. Impact sometimes has a

FIG. 5-15 The surface of the moon is covered with a layer of rock and mineral fragments (the *regolith*) pulverized by meteoroid bombardment. Astronaut Charles Conrad, Jr., of the Apollo 12 mission prepares to collect a rock specimen with special tongs that make it unnecessary for him to bend down in his pressure suit. NASA photograph.

FIG. 5-16 (Above) Coarse particles sieved from an Apollo 12 soil sample, illustrating the diversity of materials present in the soil. M, fragments of mare basalt; H, plagioclase-rich highland rock fragments; G, fragment of dark glass of mare basalt composition; K, twisted, ropy KREEP-rich glass. Millimeter scale at lower right. Smithsonian Astrophysical Observatory photograph.

FIG. 5-17 (Below) Apollo 15 soil samples being processed in an ultraclean, N_2-filled glove box in the Lunar Receiving Laboratory, NASA Manned Spacecraft Center, Houston, Texas (1971). Photograph by the author.

constructive effect, in addition to the destruction it works, in that shock pressures can act locally to weld loose soil into masses of consolidated *soil breccia*.

Lunar soil samples (Fig. 5-16) contain the products of all these processes: fragments of the underlying bedrock, soil breccias, and glassy fragments and spherules. Fragments of the impacting meteoroids are also present, but rare (less than 1 percent). The greatest proportion of glass is present in the uppermost centimeter of the soil layer, which has been affected by impacts of meteoroids of all sizes. Cosmic-ray and solar-wind effects are also most pronounced near the surface of the regolith.

All the samples returned from the moon have consisted of soil and rock fragments scooped from the regolith; none were broken from outcrops as is traditional in terrestrial field geology. Samples were returned from six landing sites on the lunar nearside by the Apollo missions to the moon, and from three additional sites by unmanned spacecraft of the Soviet Luna series (Fig. 3-19). They have been carefully processed and stored in ultraclean facilities (Fig. 5-17) to protect them from contamination for future generations of scientists to study. A five-digit numbering system is used to identify each discrete sample from the moon (Table 5-2).

Table 5-2 Numbering System Adopted for Samples Returned from the Moon by U.S. and Soviet Missions

Mission	Number
Apollo 11	10XXX
Apollo 12	12XXX
Apollo 14	14XXX
Apollo 15	15XXX
Apollo 16	6XXXX
Apollo 17	7XXXX
Luna 16	21XXX
Luna 20	22XXX
Luna 24	24XXX

Mare Basalts

Prior to the Apollo program, it was thought that the lunar surface might consist of primitive, undifferentiated planetary material, similar to the chondritic meteorites. This turned out not to be the case: all the samples returned from the moon are differentiated rocks (or breccias consisting of fragments of differentiated rocks), the products of processes of igneous fractionation that we are familiar with on Earth. The most basic discovery we have made about the moon is that it was extensively melted and chemically fractionated early in its history.

A

FIG. 5-18 Examples of lunar mare basalts. (A) "Mug shot" of basalt sample 15556 showing abundant vesicles (frozen bubbles), photographed through the window of a glove box in the Lunar Receiving Laboratory (Fig. 5-17). NASA photograph. (B) Thin section of mare basalt sample 10045 viewed by transmitted unpolarized light. The minerals are chiefly ilmenite (black), plagioclase (white), and calcic pyroxene (gray). The texture is characteristic of volcanic rocks. Smithsonian Astrophysical Observatory photograph.

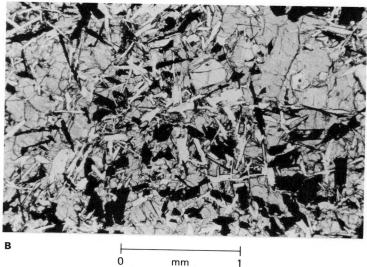

B

```
  |————————————————————|
  0        mm          1
```

All the rocks, pebbles, and lithic fragments from the soils collected on the moon can be divided into two fundamentally different compositional groups. The first of these consists of titanium-rich basalts, similar in texture and chemical composition to volcanic basaltic rocks on Earth. Rocks of this type were found wherever the dark lunar *maria* (Figs. 3-7 and 3-13) were sampled; it is now clear that these dark areas are vast lava plains, basins where floods of lava have repeatedly welled up from the lunar interior, spread, and solidified. (The second group of lunar samples, highland rocks, is discussed in the following section.)

The lunar basalts consist chiefly of clinopyroxene, ilmenite ($FeTiO_3$), and plagioclase; the mineralogy of these rocks resembles that of terrestrial basalts, exceptions being the calcium-rich character of the plagioclase (typically 85 to 95 percent anorthite), the total absence of hydrous minerals, and the exceptionally high abundance of ilmenite. Textures of the basalts (Fig. 5-18) range from fine grained and vitrophyric, such as might be expected in a basalt that chilled quickly at the surface of a flow, to coarser, microgabbroic textures that undoubtedly resulted from slower cooling deep inside a flow unit. Astrogeologic studies indicate that the maria are filled several kilometers deep with basalts in a series of flows each several tens of meters thick (Fig. 3-13).

A number of discrete families of mare basalts are recognized, differing chiefly in their content of titanium and potassium (Fig. 5-19). others that have not been sampled undoubtedly exist. Multispectral photometry (Chapter 3) makes it possible to map in detail the distribution of flows of high- and low-titanium basalts in the maria.

Terrestrial basalts are produced by partial melting in the ultramafic rock of Earth's mantle; as melting begins, the first liquid that appears has the composition of basalt. This, it appears, separates from its source region and rises to

FIG. 5-19 Differences in content of K_2O and TiO_2 of major lunar rock types. Data points are omitted; only the boundaries of clusters of points are shown. Data for mare basalts are represented by dashed boundaries; highland rock data by solid boundaries.

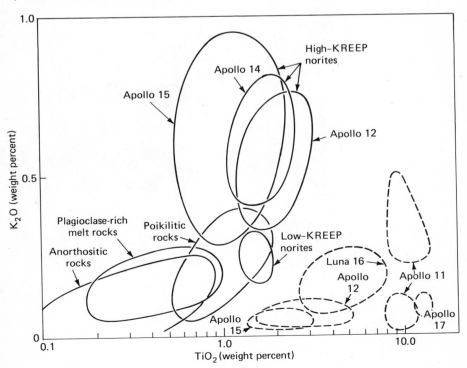

the surface before more extensive melting occurs. Lunar basalts are similarly generated. Laboratory experiments have tested the pressures and the nature of the source rocks needed to produce mare basalts by partial melting. It appears that these basalts were produced by partial melting 150 to 450 km deep in a lunar mantle of ultramafic composition.

A

0   mm   1

FIG. 5-20 Thin sections of lunar highland rocks, illustrating four principal textural categories. (A) Anorthositic breccia; consists almost entirely of calcic plagioclase clasts (60025, polarized light). (B) Melt rock with diabasic texture; plagioclase laths embedded in pyroxene (14310, polarized light).

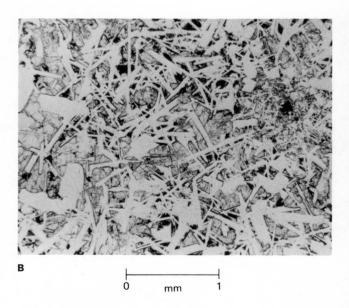

B

0   mm   1

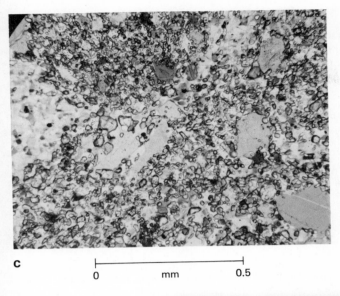

C

```
├──────────────────────┤
0          mm        0.5
```

FIG. 5-20 (cont.) (C) Anorthositic granulite, a thermally metamorphosed breccia; olivine crystals (small) and plagioclase clasts (large) in a groundmass of recrystallized plagioclase (79215, partly polarized light). (D) Poikilitic rock, in which clasts and crystallites of plagioclase are embedded in much larger regimes of optically continuous pyroxene; believed to have crystallized from a clast-laden impact melt (62235, polarized light). A fifth major highland category, polymict (mixed) breccias, is not shown. Smithsonian Astrophysical Observatory photographs.

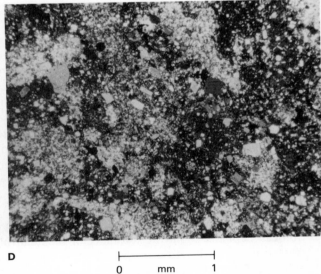

D

```
├──────────────────────┤
0          mm         1
```

Highland Rocks

The maria are surrounded and contained by older, more densely cratered terrains of a relatively light color (Fig. 3-7). Samples collected in these highland or terra regions comprise the second broad category of lunar rocks. The highland rocks were found to be rich in plagioclase and poor in ilmenite, compared to the mare basalts, accounting for their lighter color. Many are breccias (Fig. 5-20(A)), consistent with the great number of large craters in the highlands, which must have shattered and relithified the rocks repeatedly and to great depths. The compositions of highland rocks are highly variable, but most samples can be placed in one of three broad categories (Table 5-3).

Table 5-3 Principal Types of Lunar Highland Rocks

Type of Rock	Al_2O_3 Content (percent)	K_2O Content (percent)	Anorthite Content of Plagioclase (percent)
ANORTHOSITIC SUITE	>20	<0.2	>96
LOW-KREEP[a] NORITE	14–21	<0.3	92–96
HIGH-KREEP NORITE	14–21	0.3–1.0	82–94

[b]KREEP is a lunar acronym that stands for Potassium, Rare Earth Elements, and Phosphorus. These are representative of the "incompatible elements" that do not enter the major lunar rock-forming minerals, and hence are concentrated in the residual liquid when crystallization of a magma is almost completed.

Some of the KREEP-rich norites appear to be volcanic rocks, analogous to the mare basalts. They have the textures characteristic of volcanic rocks and chemical compositions suggestive of their having been generated by partial melting in a plagioclase-rich parent material (Fig. 5-21). This is not true for the rest of the highland rocks, however. Many ("Anorthositic rocks" field of Fig. 5-19) contain such high concentrations of plagioclase that they can only have been formed by some special geologic process that tended to concentrate that mineral, such as crystal fractionation in a slowly cooling magma body. Others appear to be solidified impact melts, magmas produced by the wholesale melting of whatever target rock or mixture of target rocks was struck by each of the meteoroids that produced the larger craters on the moon ("Plagioclase-rich melt rocks" and "Poikilitic rocks" fields of Fig. 5-19).

Looking beyond these variations, it appears that one important generalization can be made about the substance of the lunar highlands: it is enriched in plagioclase, and therefore in the chemical components Al_2O_3 and CaO. The oldest surface of the moon does not consist of primitive planetary material; it does not have the solar pattern of elemental abundances, as do chondritic meteorites. Clearly, the lunar surface material was produced by some process of internal fractionation of the moon after it was formed. Crystal separation is the only process we can picture that would produce the needed fractionation. It is generally believed that the surface layers of the moon (to a depth of 100 km or more) were somehow melted early in the history of that body; and as this moon-wide magma ocean cooled, crystallizing plagioclase (which has a

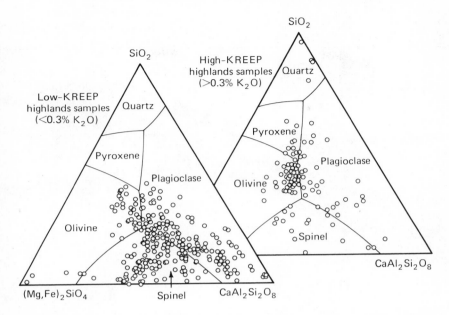

FIG. 5-21 Diagrams containing fields labeled with the first mineral to crystallize when a melt is cooled, or the last mineral to melt when a rock is heated (ternary liquidus phase diagrams). The position of a point in one of these triangles expresses its composition in terms of proportions of the three chemical components at the corners of the triangle. (The closer a point is to one of the corners, the greater its content of that component.) Compositions of lunar highland rock samples are plotted in the two triangles. The high-KREEP norites (right triangle) cluster near the intersection of the pyroxene, olivine, and plagioclase fields, a property characteristic of rocks that were generated by partial melting or were residual after fractional crystallization. It is less clear that anorthositic and other highland samples are closely related to the phase diagram (left). After J. A. Wood, *Proc. 6th Lunar Sci. Conf.*, Geochim. Cosmochim. Acta Supplement, 1975, 1087–1102.

relatively low density) tended to float upward and concentrate in what was ultimately to be the crust of the moon (Fig. 4-5). Model thermal histories of the moon generally take into account this chemical evidence that the surface layers of the moon were very hot, indeed melted, at the outset (Fig. 4-7).

Orbital Geochemistry

The previous discussion pertains to "grab samples" collected at nine points on the lunar nearside. We know something about the areal distribution of these rock types elsewhere on the moon, however, as a result of measurements made from the Apollo 15 and 16 spacecraft. As these vehicles orbited the moon, waiting for the astronauts on the lunar surface to finish their tasks, they kept

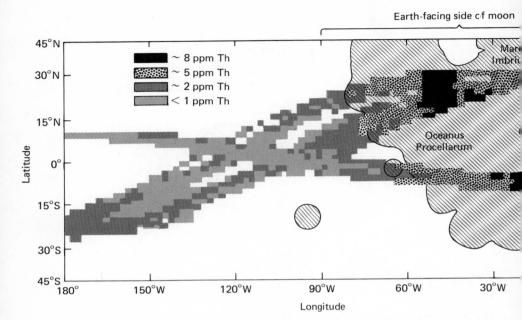

FIG. 5-22 (Above) Approximate levels of thorium in the lunar soil along ground tracks overflown by the Apollo 15 and 16 Command and Service Modules, measured by gamma-ray spectrometers carried in these spacecraft. Eight parts per million thorium is appropriate to KREEP-rich soils; < 1 ppm thorium corresponds to anorthositic soils. Diagonal hatching: mare regions. After A. E. Metzger et al., *Proc. 4th Lunar Sci. Conf.*, Geochim. Cosmochim. Acta Supplement, v. 1, Plate II 1973, (frontispiece).

instruments trained on the moon that sensed and recorded variations in the levels of several critical chemical elements as different terrains were overflown. This orbital mapping confirmed the plagioclase-rich nature of the lunar crust all the way around the moon, but it also revealed a surprise: gamma radiation due to the decay of U, Th, and ^{40}K in the regolith is not emitted symmetrically around the moon; it is concentrated in the west nearside quadrant of that body (Fig. 5-22). This probably reflects an equivalent localization of the occurrence of KREEP-rich norite, since this is the only abundant lunar rock type known that contains substantial amounts of these radioactive nuclides.

Structure and Evolution of the Moon

The internal structure of the moon is, of course, still conjectural. The deep structure, as far as it can be inferred from geophysical measurements, is shown in Fig. 4-5. Our concept of structure within the crust is based on geochemical and petrological observations; one plausible crustal model is shown in Fig. 5-23. According to this model, most of the cratering that the moon has experi-

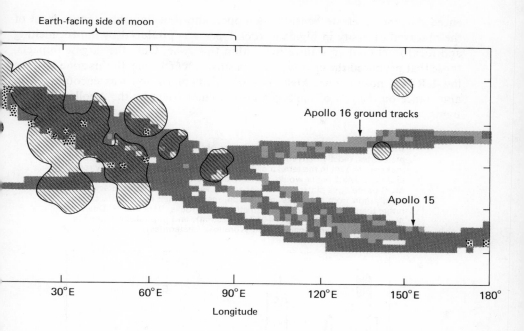

Earth-facing side of moon

Apollo 16 ground tracks

Apollo 15

30°E   60°E   90°E   120°E   150°E   180°

Longitude

FIG. 5-23 (Below) Model crustal profile for lunar highlands regions. The upper, aluminous portion must have been well mixed during the period of intense bombardment, whereas the KREEPy layer may have escaped all but a few of the larger impacts (such as the one that excavated the Serenitatis basin). Other models are possible. After G. Ryder and J. A. Wood, *Proc. 8th Lunar Sci. Conf.,* Geochim. Cosmochim. Acta Supplement, 1977, 655–668.

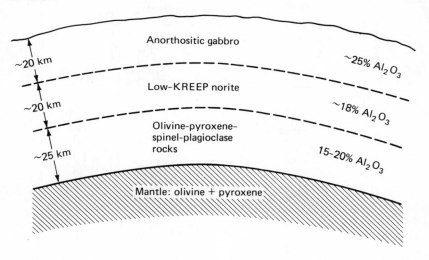

Anorthositic gabbro

~20 km

~25% Al_2O_3

Low–KREEP norite

~20 km

~18% Al_2O_3

Olivine-pyroxene-
spinel-plagioclase
rocks

~25 km

15–20% Al_2O_3

Mantle: olivine + pyroxene

enced did not penetrate beneath the upper, anorthositic gabbro zone; most of the observed diversity in highland rock types was produced by impact melting and local fractional crystallization within this zone. Only the largest impacts, those that produced the circular mare basins, reached beneath this zone into the low-KREEP norite zone. Melt rock of this composition was encountered in abundance on the rim of the Serenitatis circular basin by the Apollo 17 astronauts.

FIG. 5-24 Relative frequencies of ages of terrestrial and lunar rocks and meteorites, mostly derived by the K–Ar method. Only ages of deep-seated rocks are shown in the terrestrial histogram; inclusion of sedimentary rocks and deep-sea basalts would shift the distribution to much younger ages. Most of the ages plotted reflect secondary events that outgassed accumulated argon from the rocks in question, resetting their radiometric clocks, rather than the actual times of formation of the rocks. Data from R. Dearnly, *Nature*, v. 206, 1965, 1083–1087 (terrestrial), and unpublished compilations by G. Turner (lunar) and A. Woronow (meteorites).

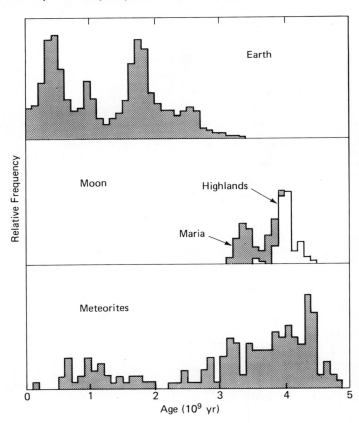

An interpretation of the evolution of any planet depends heavily on a knowledge of the ages of the rocks studied. A histogram of the ages of lunar mare basalts and highland rocks dated by the potassium–argon (K–Ar) radiometric technique is shown in Fig. 5-24. The mare basalt ages are understood to be the times when these rocks were created by partial melting beneath the crust of the moon and then erupted to the surface, but the ages of highland rocks appear to record only the last of the violent cratering events that they experienced. The concentration of highland rock ages at about 4.0×10^9 years points either to an epoch of specially intense meteoroid bombardment at that time, or, as Fig. 5-25 suggests, a bombardment rate during the entire first 0.6×10^9 years of solar-system history so intense that virtually all rocks at the lunar surface had their radiometric clocks repeatedly reset until the bombardment tapered off $\sim 4.0 \times 10^9$ years ago.

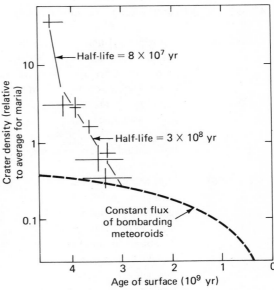

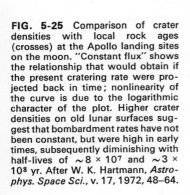

FIG. 5-25 Comparison of crater densities with local rock ages (crosses) at the Apollo landing sites on the moon. "Constant flux" shows the relationship that would obtain if the present cratering rate were projected back in time; nonlinearity of the curve is due to the logarithmic character of the plot. Higher crater densities on old lunar surfaces suggest that bombardment rates have not been constant, but were high in early times, subsequently diminishing with half-lives of $\sim 8 \times 10^7$ and $\sim 3 \times 10^8$ yr. After W. K. Hartmann, *Astrophys. Space Sci.*, v. 17, 1972, 48–64.

The meteorite and lunar sample ages compiled in Fig. 5-24 refer to the last time the rocks in question were heated to high enough temperatures to be purged of argon, thereby resetting their K–Ar radiometric clocks. Other dating techniques, especially the strontium–rubidium (Sr–Rb) and uranium, thorium–lead (U,Th–Pb) methods, record more profound events. These studies show that a major chemical fractionation occurred on the moon about 4.4×10^9 years ago. Presumably, this was the time when the lunar crust and mantle separated. The internal evolution of the moon, as it is understood at the time of writing, is summarized in Table 5-4.

Table 5-4 Internal Evolution of the Moon[a]

Time (years ago)	Event	Source of Information or Inference
4.6–4.5 × 10[9][b]	Formation of the moon; intense bombardment of the surface by planetesimals of the early solar system	By analogy with meteorite ages, and from dynamical modeling of planetary accretion
4.6–4.5 × 10[9][b]	Melting of outer layer (>100 km thick) of moon	Plagioclase-rich nature of highland rocks, presumably due to crystal fractionation; Sr–Rb model ages, U, Th–Pb and Nd–Sm dating of lunar rocks
4.5–4.4 × 10[9][b]	Cooling, crystal fractionation in "magma ocean"; continued bombardment and cratering of the lunar surface	
4.4–4.0 × 10[9][b]	Generation and upward migration of KREEP-rich magmas	Radiometric ages of KREEP-rich rocks
~4.0 × 10[9]	Major impact(s) that excavated the Imbrium Basin and possibly other basins; rapid decline in the bombardment flux at the lunar surface	^{40}Ar–^{39}Ar ages of lunar samples; crater densities on dated surfaces
4.0–3.2 × 10[9]	Generation of mare basalts by partial melting of ultramafic cumulate rocks, 150 to 450 km deep; eruption of lavas at the lunar surface	Radiometric ages of mare basalts; determination by experimental petrology of conditions that would generate such liquids by partial melting
~3.5 × 10[9]	Interior of moon has become warmer, but exterior has cooled; an outer layer (lithosphere) has become cool, thick (~200 km), and strong enough to prevent isostatic compensation of the lunar surface	"Mascons" (positive gravity anomalies) in the lunar maria, detected by perturbations that they cause in the orbits of spacecraft; thermal modeling of the moon
3.2–2.5 × 10[9][b]	Volcanism on the lunar surface ceases	Youngest lunar rocks radiometrically dated, mare surfaces with smallest crater densities
Present day	Surface cooling has thickened the lithosphere to ~1,000 km; zone of partial melting has moved to deep interior, probably concentrating a small sulfide-plus-metal core at the center	Seismology; thermal modeling

[a]As perceived at the time of writing.
[b]Range of ages expresses uncertainty rather than duration of the process.

Bulk Composition of the Moon

It might seem futile to try to infer the overall composition of a differentiated planet like the moon (or Earth, for that matter) if one has access only to
samples from the outermost layer. However, it is possible to make broad generalizations. The moon is depleted in the relatively volatile elements, relative to
Earth. This can be demonstrated by comparing elemental abundances in lunar
and terrestrial basalts, both of which are derived by partial melting from the
mantles of their respective planets (Fig. 5-26). The total absence of water in the
minerals and rocks of the moon is a particularly dramatic illustration of the
depletion of volatiles in that body.

It is also clear from the relatively small size of the lunar core (if it has one
at all; Fig. 4-5) and the low mean density of the moon that it is depleted in iron.
Analyses of lunar samples make it appear that the moon is depleted in all
members of the siderophile or "iron-loving" class of elements (i.e., Fe, Ni, Co,
and many trace elements such as Pt, Pd, Ir) relative to Earth. On the other
hand, it appears from the composition and extent of the lunar crust that our
satellite is probably somewhat enriched in the particularly involatile elements
(e.g., Al, Ca, Ti, Ba, Sr, U). These are the elements that would be first to condense from a cooling solar nebula (Chapter 7).

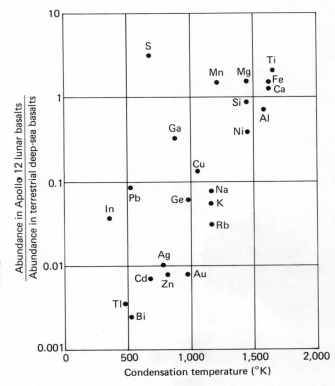

FIG. 5-26 Relative abundances
of elements in lunar and terrestrial basalts versus volatility of
the elements (in terms of the
temperatures at which they
would condense from the solar
nebula). The most volatile elements are systematically depleted in the moon, relative to
Earth.

Bombardment History of the Moon

Many elements of the lunar terrain, especially the maria, were hot and relatively smooth when they were first laid down. Subsequently, they cooled and began to record radiometric time; they also accumulated impact craters. For those areas that were explored by the Apollo astronauts, it is now possible to compare crater densities with ages of deposition of the surfaces (determined by radiometric dating of returned samples; Fig. 5-25), and thus to learn the variability of the cratering rate with time. It is clear that the cratering rate during the first 10^9 years of lunar history was much higher than it is now. (If the cratering rate had been the same through all geologic time as it is now, data points in Fig. 5-25 would all fall on the "constant flux" curve.) The decline in the early cratering rate was rapid; in the period when the mare basalts were erupted, it "decayed" with a half-life of $\sim 3 \times 10^8$ years; that is, every 3×10^8 years the rate at which meteoroids were colliding with the moon halved. Prior to the epoch of mare emplacement, the lunar highlands were bombarded by a population of meteoroids whose abundance in space decayed at an even more rapid rate.

This reading of the impact history of the moon provides valuable insight into the abundance and rate of capture of small bodies and planetary debris in the early solar system (Chapter 7).

six

the sun and stars

THE SUN

Turning finally to the central and most massive member of the solar system, we find a huge rotating sphere of white-hot gases. The sun is 109 times as large (diameter) as Earth, and 333,000 times as massive (solar radius, 6.96 $\times$ 10^5 km; solar mass, 1.99 $\times$ 10^{33} g). Since it is a fluid rather than a solid body, not all parts of the sun turn at the same rate. Material near the equator rotates once every $\sim$25 Earth days; near the poles, rotation takes $\sim$29 days. The sun turns with the same (direct) sense of rotation as the planetary orbits, about an axis that is very nearly perpendicular to the orbital planes of the planets (7.2° from the normal to the ecliptic plane). The mean density of the sun is 1.4 g/cm³; its moment-of-inertia factor is 0.06, indicating a very high degree of mass concentration near the center.

The white-hot layer of the sun that is normally visible to us, the *photosphere*, is composed largely of neutral gas atoms at a temperature of $\sim$5,700°K. The photosphere and immediately adjacent layers of the sun are in continuous turbulent motion (Fig. 6-1). The supergranulation, a pattern of huge convection cells that covers most or all of the sun at any given time, is caused by the flow of heat outward from the solar interior; other more sporadic features (sunspots, prominences, flares) are the effects of irregularities in the behavior of the sun's magnetic field.

The sun is surrounded by a *corona* of ionized gas, which is clearly visible only when the dazzling solar photosphere is eclipsed, as by the moon (Fig. 6-2). The corona is very tenuous and much hotter than the photosphere, approximately 2,600,000°K. This seems paradoxical or even impossible: heat flows from

127

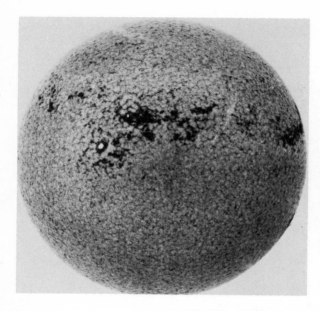

FIG. 6-1 (Left) Negative image of the sun, as it appears when light of only one particular wavelength (in this case corresponding to a spectral line of ionized Calcium) is admitted to the camera. Under these conditions surface detail becomes visible that cannot be seen by full-spectrum sunlight. Most of the solar surface is covered with huge thermal convection cells, the *supergranulation*. Transitory localized heating of the chromosphere produces *plages* (dark regions). Sunspots (bright in negative image, cool, also transient) contain magnetic fields of exceptional strength. Hale Observatories photograph.

FIG. 6-2 The solar corona, a halo of extremely hot ionized gases visible only during eclipses of the sun. Lick Observatory photograph.

hot to cooler places, so how can the relatively cool sun maintain its corona at this high temperature? The answer appears to be that the corona derives its energy not from the heat but from the interior convective motions of the sun. Some of this mechanical energy is propagated outward (perhaps in the form of shock waves) through the chromosphere and corona, where it is ultimately converted to heat. (The *chromosphere* is a transitional layer, about 2,500 km thick, between the cool, neutral photosphere and the hot, ionized corona.)

The corona has no outer boundary, nor is it static; the coronal plasma is continually expanding outward into space. At 1 AU, outward-streaming ions from the solar corona constitute a *solar wind* that sweeps past Earth at 300 to 600 km/sec. The present-day solar wind is detected by satellites, and manifests itself by "blowing" the gas tails of comets outward from the sun (Fig. 2-13) and promoting auroral displays and magnetic storms in Earth's atmosphere. Accumulations of recent solar wind gases are present in lunar soil samples, and gases of the ancient solar wind are preserved in some meteorites.

The energy unceasingly radiated from the surface of the sun is understood to be generated by nuclear fusion reactions deep inside the sun. These reactions occur when matter is made hot enough and is held close enough together, as by the enormous pressure at the center of the sun. The dominant energy-producing reaction in the sun, the proton–proton chain, is illustrated in Fig. 6-3.

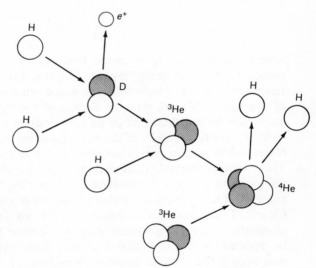

FIG. 6-3 The proton–proton chain, the dominant energy-producing nuclear fusion reaction in the solar interior. 175,000 kWh of energy is released for every gram of ^4He produced. (D stands for deuterium, e^+ for a positron.)

We attempt to understand the internal structure of the sun by setting up and testing models, in much the same manner as planetary interiors are modeled (Chapter 4). In some ways it is easier to model a star than a planet. For one thing, it is fairly safe to assume that the sun is compositionally homogeneous (except for an enhanced helium/hydrogen ratio in its deep interior, as a result of fusion reactions), and that the observed surface composition of the sun is representative of its interior. Also, the equation of state (the relationship between pressure, temperature, and density) of a hot gas is simpler and better understood than that of solid rock or metal.

The principal complication lies in defining the opacity of solar matter to radiative energy, and therefore the ease or difficulty with which heat is passed outward from the deep interior to the surface of the sun. The opacity of gases at any depth in the sun is a function of the temperature and pressure at that point; these determine the degree to which the gases absorb and reemit, or scatter, radiation at various wavelengths.

There are two fundamentally different modes of heat transport in the sun, depending upon the steepness of the thermal gradient (degrees Kelvin per kilometer of depth). To understand the situations that they apply to, let us consider a volume of gas of just one gram mass at a point in the sun where the temperature is T_1 and the pressure is P_1. If the gram of gas were moved to a higher position in the sun under conditions such that it could expand or contract readily, but could not gain or lose heat to its surroundings (say it was contained in an insulating jacket), it would of course expand until its pressure equaled the new local pressure (P_2, say). The gram of gas would also adopt a new temperature, T_2, simply by virtue of its expansion. The *adiabatic* (i.e., insulated against heat exchange) relationship between old and new temperatures and pressures is

$$\frac{T_1}{T_2} = \left(\frac{P_1}{P_2}\right)^{(\gamma-1)/\gamma} \tag{6-1}$$

where γ is the ratio between the heat capacities at constant pressure and at constant volume for the solar gas (c_p/c_v). If it turned out that the new expanded temperature T_2 was greater than the temperature of the surrounding solar gases at this new high level, then the density of the hypothetical gram of insulated gas would be less than that of its surroundings (since the density ratio $\rho_2/\rho_1 = T_1/T_2$, for two samples of the same gas at the same pressure), and so buoyant forces would tend to propel the gram of gas even higher. If not, it would sink. The particular thermal gradient along which Eq. (6-1) is exactly obeyed (so that after a volume of gas is transferred to a new depth and allowed to expand or contract, it has no tendency either to rise or sink) is called the *adiabatic gradient*. Clearly, if the actual thermal gradient in the sun were steeper than the adiabatic gradients, volumes of gas would everywhere begin to rise toward the surface, to be replaced by cooler gas that descended from higher levels. This would be the case even if the artificial assumption of insulating jackets on volumes of gas were removed, since rising masses of gas could not exchange heat with their surroundings instantly even without them. For this reason the thermal gradient in the sun *cannot* be steeper than the adiabatic gradient: wherever the latter is slightly exceeded, convective motion of the type just described sets in and, by efficient transport of heat, reduces the thermal gradient just *to* the adiabatic gradient.

Returning now to the two modes of heat transfer mentioned above, one of these holds where the opacity of the solar material is low; here energy moves outward by being literally shined through the solar gases, and the thermal gradient remains small. Where the opacity is high, however, and the escape of energy is hindered, temperatures at depth mount and the thermal gradient increases. If the adiabatic gradient is exceeded, the system becomes unstable against convection, and heat is moved outward by the actual physical transport of hot gases to the surface of the sun where their heat can be radiated to space. This is the second available mode of heat transport.*

A successful model of the solar interior has to satisfy these conditions:

1. Pressure, temperature, and density must increase inward, beginning with values observed in the solar photosphere.

2. Pressure, temperature, and density of the solar gases must everywhere be related by the equation of state that is appropriate to this material.

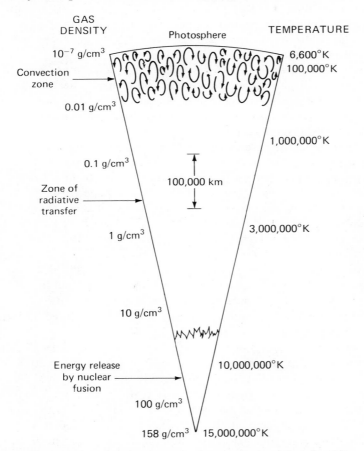

FIG. 6-4 Schematic depth profile in the sun, from model studies. After E. G. Gibson, *The Quiet Sun*, NASA SP-303, Washington, D.C., 1973.

*This concept is just as applicable to solid planets as to the sun. Heat is transferred in planets by conduction unless the adiabatic gradient of the rock is exceeded, whereupon solid-state convection can occur if the rock is hot and "soft" enough. Depending upon the effective viscosity of the rock, the convection may be so sluggish as to have a negligible effect on heat transport; or it may comprise an important second mode of heat transport, as in the sun.

3. At every level, pressure of the gas must be just great enough to support the weight of overlying layers; no more or less.

4. Pressure and temperature in the deep interior must be at values that would promote a rate of nuclear fusion adequate to generate the amount of energy the sun is observed to radiate. It is not simply a matter of specifying the central temperature; the net effect of opacities throughout the body of the sun has to be to conserve enough of the heat that is being generated to hold the interior temperature at the appropriate value. These interior opacities are in turn sensitive to local temperatures and pressures in the model.

5. The model must reproduce the sun's dimension, mean density, and moment-of-inertia factor.

The model shown in Fig. 6-4 satisfies these conditions. It consists of a central "core" in which nuclear fusion reactions generate heat, a thick shell at intermediate depths that is transparent enough to transmit heat outward by radiation, and an outermost shell in which the thermal gradient is so steep that convective heat transport occurs.

In one respect, however, this and other relatively simple solar models do not appear to correspond to the real sun. The fusion reactions in the core of the sun, according to the models, should generate neutrinos at a calculable rate. Neutrinos are subatomic particles that would escape virtually unchecked through the body of the sun; a certain proportion of them should reach the earth, which they can also penetrate effortlessly. They have a very small but calculable probability of reacting with chlorine atoms that they encounter, transforming stable ^{37}Cl into radioactive ^{37}Ar (half-life, 35 days). If a very large amount of chlorine could be put in a place where it was shielded from cosmic rays (which also convert ^{37}Cl to ^{37}Ar), and its miniscule output of ^{37}Ar was periodically harvested and measured with ultrasensitive radiation counters, the flux of neutrinos from the center of the sun could be monitored on Earth.

This has actually been done, by placing 100,000 gallons of cleaning fluid (tetrachloroethylene, C_2Cl_4) in a tank in a gold mine, a mile deep in the earth where cosmic rays cannot penetrate (Fig. 6-5). To the consternation of astrophysicists, the amount of ^{37}Ar being produced in this cleaning fluid corresponds to a flux of neutrinos no greater than one tenth of that predicted by solar models. Clearly, there is some major flaw in our conception of the workings of the sun. Efforts to understand the discrepancy have tended to question the assumption of stability and steady evolution of the sun inherent in the models. Instabilities could lead to periodic fluctuations in the rate of nuclear fusion and neutrino generation in the solar interior. In particular, it has been proposed that mixing occurs periodically between the ^4He-rich core of the sun and the cooler overlying layers, rich in H and ^3He. This would promote a surge of energy generation and a temperature rise in the solar interior. The latter would then expand and energy generation would diminish until the excess heat had dissipated, whereupon the core would contract and the rate of fusion reaction would increase again. According to this hypothesis, the core of the sun is currently in the expanded state and the nuclear fires have been banked.

FIG. 6-5 Solar neutrino detector: a tank of cleaning fluid 1 mile deep in the Homestake gold mine, South Dakota. Photograph courtesy of R. Davis, Jr., and the Brookhaven National Laboratory.

If the rate of energy generation fluctuates in the sun, so must its rate of energy emission (the solar luminosity); the planets must now be experiencing lower-than-average surface temperatures. It has been suggested that glacial periods in Earth's history correlate with lows in the sun's nuclear fusion–energy emission cycle. The current presence of ice caps at Earth's poles, where there has not always been ice, may be related to the low neutrino flux from the sun. So might the present waterless state of Mars. At other times, when the sun warmed the Martian surface to higher temperatures, the melting of polar and subsurface ice may have provided the flow of liquid water that eroded stream channels on the surface of that planet (Fig. 3-14). This relationship between cyclic behavior of the sun and planets must be considered highly tentative, however. The discrepancy between predicted and observed solar neutrino fluxes is very large, and associated luminosity variations would be much greater than Earth seems to have experienced. The fact is that the state and behavior of the sun are not well understood at present.

THE STARS

Our galaxy contains 47×10^9 masses of hot luminous gas more or less similar to the sun. The stars appear only as points of light in a telescope, so it might seem very little could be learned about them. However, this is not the case. The brightness of each star can be measured with sensitive photoelectric cells; when a correction is made for the distance to the star, its brightness can be expressed in terms of total energy output (ergs/per second), or luminosity relative to that of the sun ($L/L_\odot$). (Distances to the stars are derived by a variety of ingenious methods, not described here because of space limitations.)

The spectra of the radiation from individual stars can also be taken. These are rich in information. Among other things, the surface temperature of a star can be determined from its spectrum by several methods. The overall shape of its continuous emission spectrum (Fig. 6-6) is a function of a star's temperature; the hotter the star, the larger the proportion of its energy that is radiated at short wavelengths. Hot stars tend to be bluish, cooler stars reddish. Also, the character of the absorption spectrum (the spectral class) expresses temperature. Higher temperatures excite the electrons associated with atoms in stellar atmospheres to higher energy levels, and this gives rise to additional absorption lines in the star's spectrum.

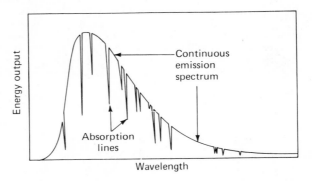

FIG. 6-6 The spectrum of a main-sequence star; schematic. This consists of a *continuous emission spectrum* upon which is superimposed the lines of an *absorption spectrum*. A continuous spectrum is emitted by hot solids, liquids, or gases at moderate to high pressures (e.g., the sun's photosphere). The wavelength of peak energy emission is inversely proportional to temperature. If the continuous emission spectrum passes through a layer of cooler low-pressure gas (such as the chromosphere of the sun or a star), the latter absorbs radiation at certain wavelengths that are characteristic of the temperature of the absorbing layer and the elements present in it.

It is instructive to set up a plot of luminosity versus temperature (this is named a Hertzsprung–Russell or H–R diagram), and enter points in it representing a large number of stars (Figs. 6-7 and 6-8). Stars in such a diagram do not scatter at random, but cluster strongly in a diagonal belt (the *main sequence*). A pronounced grouping of *red giants* also appears above the main sequence.

Stars are dispersed in the heaverns not only singly, but often in pairs. Both members of each *binary* system orbit about the center of gravity of the pair. If it is possible to measure the dimensions and period of the two orbits about their common center of mass, the mass of each member can be calculated from the laws of dynamics (Eq. (2-1)). By this means it has been possible to derive the masses of a number of main-sequence stars, and a clear relationship has emerged

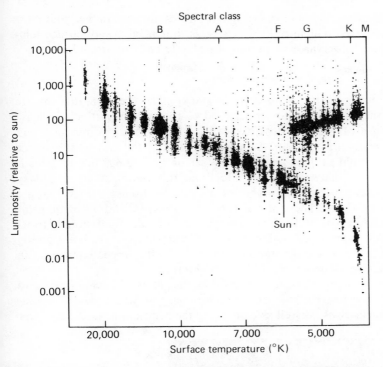

FIG. 6-7 (Above) A Hertzsprung–Russell diagram compiled in 1936, containing all stars for which spectral class and luminosity were known at the time. The striped appearance of the plot is a consequence of the finite number of spectral classes and subclasses that have been defined; actually there is a smooth distribution of stars with surface temperature. Figure by W. Gyllenberg, Lund Observatory, Sweden.

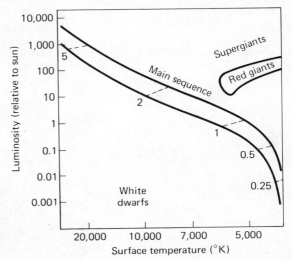

FIG. 6-8 (Right) Names applied to principal groupings of stars in Fig. 6-7. Numbers refer to the masses of individual stars in the main sequence relative to the mass of the sun.

between their masses and luminosities (Fig. 6-8). It is obvious, in fact, that most stars are well-ordered machines in which mass, luminosity, and surface temperature, the three observable properties, are closely and predictably related.

Formation and Early Evolution of Stars

Stars are not permanent fixtures in the galaxy. They are born, they mature and age, and they die. Stars are understood to form from particulary dense interstellar clouds of gas and dust, typically ~ 10 parsecs in dimension and $\sim 10^4$ times as massive as our sun. A parsec, pc, 3.13×10^{13} km, is the distance at which 1 AU would subtend an angle of 1 sec of arc, 1/3,600 degree. This is the standard unit of stellar distances. Clouds of this character in our galaxy (Fig. 6-9) are observed to contain types of stars, to be discussed later, that are known to be very young. Thermal and turbulent pressures and magnetic fields in interstellar clouds tend to keep them dispersed; mutual gravitational attraction tends to pull them together. Under some circumstances, which are poorly understood at present, self-gravitational forces gain the upper hand and an interstellar cloud or portion thereof begins to contract.

As contraction proceeds, it appears that the interstellar cloud tends to fragment into progressively smaller subunits, many of which continue contracting upon themselves, as well as continuing their motion toward the center

FIG. 6-9 The Great Nebula in Orion, a dense cloud of gas and dust 10 to 30 parsecs in diameter in which star formation is believed to be occurring. Four young, hot stars (spectral classes O and B) provide most of the light that illuminates the nebula. Lick Observatory photograph.

FIG. 6-10 The Praesepe open cluster of stars in the constellation Cancer. Members of the cluster can be distinguished from nonmembers that lie in the same star field by the fact that the former all move in the same direction at the same velocity. Members of a given cluster are thought to have formed from a single batch of "raw material" (interstellar gas and dust). Harvard College Observatory photograph.

of mass of the original cloud. The contracting cloud fragments become a cluster of stars. The process is inefficient; only a small fraction (0.1 to 1 percent) of the gas and dust in an interstellar cloud is likely to be converted to stars in a particular episode of star formation. It might seem that, since cloud fragments (later to become stars) are falling under the forces of mutual gravitation toward the center of the cloud (later the star cluster), they will end up in a grand collision. Because the original cloud would have had some rotational motion, however, stars condensing from it would not fall directly toward the center of the cloud, but into orbits around its center of mass. Collisions would be rare. Star clusters persist for a time (Fig. 6-10), but do not have long-term dynamic stability; one by one, member stars are ejected from clusters at greater than the escape velocity. The sun is not a member of a star cluster.

Let us follow the contraction of one particular cloud fragment. Modeling studies indicate that the contraction would be nonuniform: the inner portion of the cloud fragment collapses most rapidly, forming a dense central condensation. Matter from farther out in the fragment continues to fall into this central condensation for some time afterward.

At first, elements of the cloud fragment are in free fall toward the center of mass of the fragment. There is nothing to stop them; gas pressures are too low. Pressure mounts as the contraction proceeds, but so do self-gravitational forces in the fragment, since the elements of gas and dust that are exerting gravitational forces on one another are coming closer together. Compression of the gas generates heat, but as long as the contracting gas remains transparent to radiation the heat energy is dissipated to space, and the temperature of the gas (initially $\sim 10°K$) does not increase substantially.

Eventually, the central portion or core of the contracting system becomes more opaque to radiation, however, simply because of close crowding of the gas and especially the dust particles. Then temperature in the core begins to mount and, with it, pressure. A point is reached when gas pressures in the dense core of the cloud fragment counterbalance the forces of self-gravitation, whereupon rapid contraction of this core (which we now call a *protostar*) ceases.

Material from farther out in the cloud fragment continues to fall onto the surface of the protostar, generating heat as it does so. The protostar grows larger, and its surface becomes hotter and more luminous (Fig. 6-11). When most of the cloud fragment material has been incorporated and the infall rate diminishes, the surface temperature and luminosity probably decrease.

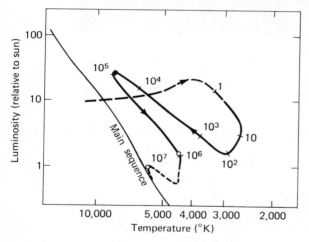

FIG. 6-11 Evolution in the H–R diagram of a protostar that forms from a one-solar-mass cloud fragment, according to the modeling of R. B. Larson. Numbers along the track are elapsed time, in years. Between about 10^2 and 10^6 yr, surface heating by infalling cloud material dominates the thermal structure of the star. Accretion by infall is half completed at $\sim 10^5$ yr. Hydrogen fusion occurs in the short-dashed portion of the track. After R. B. Larson, *Monthly Not. Roy. Astron. Soc.*, v. 157, 1972, 121–145.

At this point the effect of infalling matter ceases to dominate the energy budget of the protostar; its internal structure becomes more important. The protostar would have a quasi-stable internal structure much like that discussed earlier for the sun, with temperature and density increasing with depth in such a way that gas pressure is everywhere just adequate to support the weight of overlying layers. The most important difference would be that the central temperature of the protostar is not nearly as high as that of the sun; not high enough, in fact, to promote nuclear fusion reactions. Thus heat radiated from the surface of the protostar is not replaced by fusion-generated heat, so the system would tend to cool down. Interior cooling means a decrease in gas pressure; the balance between pressure and gravitational forces is destroyed, so the protostar contracts to a smaller size; this compresses the gases further and raises temperatures again (to higher values than previously, in fact); gas pressure and gravitational forces balance once again, but only temporarily, as heat continues to be lost from the protostar and a new cycle of contraction begins.

Actually, the above presentation of protostar contraction as a series of discrete shrinkages is artificial. A system of this type would contract continuously and smoothly, at just such a rate that continuing compression of its interior generates exactly enough heat to replace losses and maintain the interior gases at high enough temperatures and pressures to stave off collapse. This process is known as *Helmholtz-Kelvin* contraction.

Protostars at various stages of contraction can be modeled, just as the solar interior can (previous section). Interior and surface temperatures are found to increase as the protostar becomes smaller and denser. A central temperature is eventually reached ($\sim 10^7 {}^\circ$K) at which hydrogen fusion reactions begin to occur. Thereafter, the stellar structure is stabilized, because further contraction does not need to occur to replace the energy being radiated from the surface of the star. The star remains in a nearly constant configuration for a long time, until the balance is upset by exhaustion of the supply of hydrogen in its deep interior. This condition of quasi-stability is attained when stars of various masses have reached the main sequence in the H–R diagram. That is why the main sequence is so densely populated; stars spend most of their lives there, in the "hydrogen-burning" phase of their evolution.

Can real examples be found in the heavens of infant stars that occupy pre-main-sequence positions in the H–R diagram (Fig. 6-11)? The major cluster of red giants in Fig. 6-7 corresponds to stars in late stages of evolution (discussed in the next section), not early. Young stars tend to be inconspicuous because they are surrounded and obscured by dense clouds of gas and dust. Several classes of young stars or manifestations of stars have been identified, however, that lie in the appropriate regions of the H–R diagram. These are given the names T Tauri stars, Herbig emission stars, Herbig–Haro objects, and embedded infrared sources. (Radiation from very young protostars is absorbed by dust particles in surrounding clouds of infalling material. The dust reradiates the energy at infrared wavelengths.) Young stars have a number of interesting properties, but two are of particular importance. First, they tend to be irregularly variable in brightness on a short time scale (days or less); there is an unstable element in their behavior. Second, detailed analysis of their spectra shows that ionized gas appears to be streaming away from them at a rapid rate, 10^{-6} to 10^{-5} of a solar mass per year. Since stars are believed to spend a fraction of a million years of their youth in this stage of plasma emission, they may end up losing a substantial proportion of their original masses. Variability of luminosity and mass outflow are not predicted or explained by modeling studies; they are observational facts.

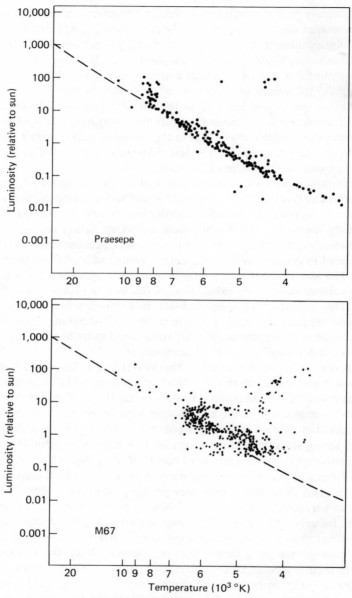

FIG. 6-12 H–R diagrams, showing members of two star clusters. In the Praesepe cluster, few stars have "peeled away" from the main sequence to the red-giant region; Praesepe is a young cluster, only ~250 million yr old. In the older (~4,000 million yr) M67 cluster, many more stars have evolved to the red giant region. After H. C. Arp in *Astrophysics II: Stellar Structures,* S. Flügge, ed., v. 51 of *Handbuch der Physik* (New York: Springer-Verlag, 1958), 75–133.

Late Evolution and the Final Fate of Stars

In the later stages of their evolution, stars move off the main sequence and into the region of the H–R diagram populated by giant and supergiant stars. We gather this from studies of star clusters (Fig. 6-10). Since each cluster is believed to have formed from a single cloud of parent material, the stars that comprise it should have essentially identical compositions and "birth dates." Figure 6-12 shows H–R diagrams of the stars in two clusters, Praesepe and M67. In both cases the smaller, less luminous stars follow the main sequence faithfully. But a few of the brightest Praesepe stars, those 10 times or more as luminous as the sun, seem to be detached from the main sequence. The dissaffection is more pronounced in M67; here almost all the stars more luminous than the sun have "peeled away" from the main sequence and shifted rightward, into the red giant region. Once having left the main sequence, the brightest stars appear to have migrated farthest. Evidently, M67 is an older, more evolved cluster than Praesepe.

It appears that the most luminous stars (those high in the H–R diagram) reside for the shortest time on the main sequence. It is easy to see why they would evolve most rapidly; Fig. 6-8 shows that main-sequence stars emitting energy 1,000 times as fast as the sun are only about five times as massive, and thus contain only five times as much nuclear "fuel" as the sun. Obviously, these luminous stars must deplete their fuel and suffer important changes in internal composition sooner than stars lower on the main sequence.

Model studies indicate that stars follow two basically different patterns of late evolution, depending upon their masses. When small stars (less than about four times the mass of the sun) have exhausted the supply of hydrogen in their deep interiors, internal readjustments begin to take place. If the H-fusion source of heat were turned off, the star would resume the process of Helmholtz–Kelvin contraction described earlier, producing heat and even higher internal temperatures by the additional compression of its gases. These higher temperatures, however, would promote the ignition of H-burning in shallower but still H-rich levels of the star that had been too cool previously to sustain fusion reactions. This is essentially what happens when stars exhaust their core hydrogen, although no sequence of exhaustion, contraction, and reignition occurs; H-burning proceeds smoothly from the core to the shell surrounding the core, and with time the H-burning shell works its way higher and higher into the star's H-rich mantle. At the same time, the stellar interior contracts and becomes progressively hotter.

Eventually, the stellar core becomes so hot ($\sim 10^8 °K$) that helium, the "ashes" of the H-burning reactions, begins to participate in a new type of energy-generating fusion reaction. (Hydrogen-burning is only the first in a series of possible fusion reactions, involving progressively heavier fuel and product nuclei and higher temperatures needed to initiate and sustain the reaction; Table 6-1.)

Table 6-1 Stages of Nuclear Energy Generation

Name of Process	Fuel	Products	Approximate Temperature (°K)
HYDROGEN-BURNING	H	He	$1–3 \times 10^7$
HELIUM-BURNING	He	C, O	2×10^8
CARBON-BURNING	C	O, Ne, Na, Mg	8×10^8
NEON-BURNING	Ne	O, Mg	1.5×10^9
OXYGEN-BURNING	O	Mg to S	2×10^9
SILICON-BURNING	Mg to S	Elements near Fe	3×10^9

From A. G. W. Cameron, 1976, in Frontiers of Astrophysics, *E. H. Avrett ed.* (Harvard University Press), *554 pp.*

Once simple core H-burning ends for a star, and it evolves to more complex structures and processes, the star leaves its position of stability on the main sequence and begins to migrate in the H–R diagram (Figs. 6-13 and 6-14.) Since contraction and heating is occurring, it might seem that the star would move leftward in the diagram to higher temperatures; but model studies show that core contraction is accompanied by expansion of the overlying stellar envelope. Since the star's energy output is being radiated from a much larger surface area, the temperature of that surface actually decreases, moving the star right in the H–R diagram to the red giant region.

FIG. 6-13 Interior of a small star (less than four solar masses) while it is on the main sequence (left), and after it has evolved into a red giant (right). Schematic; actually a red giant is 10 to 20 times larger in diameter than its mainsequence precursor.

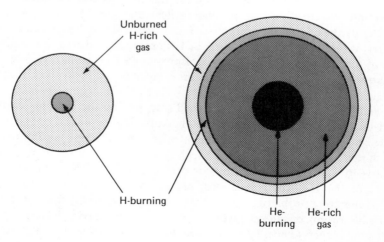

Unburned H-rich gas

H-burning

He-burning

He-rich gas

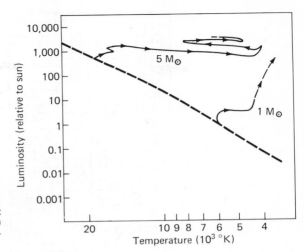

FIG. 6-14 Evolution in the H–R diagram of a one-solar-mass and a five-solar-mass star after they exhaust the supply of hydrogen at their cores and leave the main sequence. After I. Iben, *Science*, v. 155, 1967, 785–796.

The process of evolution described is thought to come to an end when the H-burning shell works its way so close to the surface of the star that radiation pressure from this hot layer is able to lift off and blow away the remaining thin skin of unburned hydrogen. *Planetary nebulae* (Fig. 6-15), which are fairly abundant in the galaxy, appear to represent this stage of stellar evolution.

FIG. 6-15 The planetary nebula NGC 7293 in the constellation Lyra, an expanding shell of gases roughly 20,000 AU in diameter. Structures of this type, which are fairly abundant in our galaxy, are believed to represent a late stage of evolution of small stars when hydrogen burning has worked its way so near to the stellar surface that the radiative energy generated is able to blow away the remaining layer of unburned hydrogen. Kitt Peak National Observatory photograph.

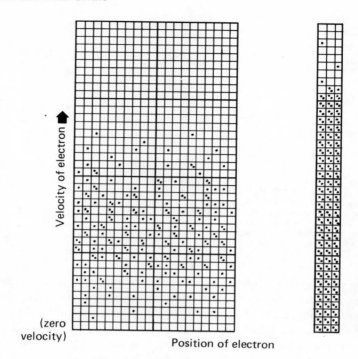

FIG. 6-16 Schematic representation of electron degeneracy. The state of an electron can be expressed by three numbers describing its position in space, and the three components of its momentum vector (proportional to velocity). One other number specifies its direction of spin. The total range of possibilities for electrons can be expressed in six-dimensional space (three dimensions for position, three for momentum). According to quantum mechanics, this *phase space* is divided into discrete cells or boxes, each of dimension h^3 (h, the Planck constant, = 6.625 × 10^{-27} g·cm²/sec), and no more than two electrons can occupy any cell at a given time. The two electrons must have opposite directions of spin. This figure uses two-dimensional paper to approximate six-dimensional phase space.

 Left: At low densities, the electrons (dots) in an ionized gas have an abundance of cells at their disposal; at any moment they occupy these in such a way that their velocities correspond to a Maxwell distribution. (This is the same law that governs the velocities of gas atoms in atmospheres, shown in Fig. 4-8.) The average electron velocity is a function of temperature; if the gas were cooled, the momentary distribution of velocities would move to a position lower in the diagram. *Right:* If the same system is compressed to very high densities, however, there is a smaller range of positions available to the electrons. Effectively, the number of available cells in phase space diminishes. The same number of electrons shown in the left diagram would be forced to fill all cells in the lower range of velocities. But now the velocity distribution cannot respond to a decrease in temperature, since it has already "hit bottom"; the electron gas continues to maintain a distribution of velocities up to high values, and to exert a correspondingly high pressure, no matter how low the temperature falls. Such a system is said to be *degenerate.*

With its H-burning shell extinguished, the remnant core of the star cools to the point where the He-burning reaction in its depths cannot be sustained either. Thereafter, the star has no remaining sources of nuclear energy. It might seem that resumed Helmholtz–Kelvin contraction would sooner or later produce internal temperatures high enough to restart He-burning or promote some other fusion reaction, but this does not happen. By now, the star, a *white dwarf*, has already contracted to the point where it is no bigger than Earth, and has a mean density of $\sim 10^6$ g/cm³. At these extreme densities the equation of state of matter that provides the basis for Helmholtz–Kelvin contraction, that is, the perfect gas law, is no longer applicable. A new type of pressure, due to degeneracy of the free electrons in the ionized stellar gas (Fig. 6-16), comes into play. A gas of degenerate electrons exerts a pressure that is independent of temperature, and in stellar remnants less than ~ 1.2 times as massive as the sun this pressure is sufficient to counterbalance self-gravitational forces no matter how much the star cools down. As its residual heat is dissipated, a white dwarf becomes cooler and less luminous, until it is no longer visible. It spends the rest of eternity as a cold, inert mass of, chiefly, degenerate helium—a black dwarf.

Stars more than four times as massive as the sun evolve beyond core He-burning. They form He-burning shells concentrically inside their H-burning shells, and eventually their cores become hot enough to initiate yet another fusion reaction, C-burning. This can happen repeatedly, creating more and more concentric shells of nuclear burning (Fig. 6-17), until all the fusion reactions of Table 6-1 are at work in the star. The more massive the star, the more

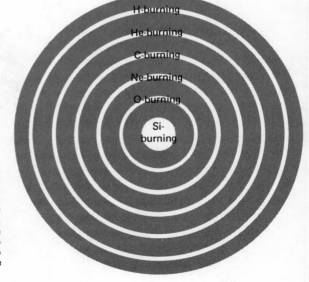

FIG. 6-17 Internal structure of a massive, highly evolved supergiant star; schematic. Six different energy-generating nuclear fusion reactions are in operation. In the (shaded) layer between any two nuclear-burning shells, material is too depleted in the fuel being burned in the outer shell to participate in that reaction, and too cool to participate in the burning of the next inner shell.

levels of nuclear burning it engages. During this time, the star wanders about the supergiant region of the H–R diagram.

The electrons of the material at the core of a supergiant form a degenerate gas, and the pressure of this gas supports the overlying layers of the star. As contraction proceeds and the density of the core exceeds $\sim 10^8$ g/cm^3, electrons are pressed into such intimate contact with nuclei that they begin to react with protons in them, forming neutrons. This subtraction of electrons from the degenerate gas diminishes the supportive pressure exerted by the gas, leading to more contraction, even higher densities, additional removal of electrons by reaction with protons, and so forth; the net effect is a sudden collapse of the stellar core that had been supported by electron degeneracy. The overlying material of course collapses with it, temperatures everywhere catapult, and unburned nuclear fuels are suddenly reacted. The result is an explosion, a *supernova* (Fig. 6-18) that scatters most of the substance of the star into interstellar space.

FIG. 6-18 Cassiopeia A, debris of a supernova that exploded about 1660 A.D. (negative image). Arrows show the distance each gas concentration will travel in the next 50 yr. Spectra of the fragments show that they are chemically dissimilar, presumably derived from different shells in the supergiant that exploded. Fragments that emit strongly at wavelengths characteristic of oxygen and sulfur, respectively, are labeled O and S. From K. Kamper and S. van den Bergh, *Sky and Telescope*, v. 51, 1976, 236–239.

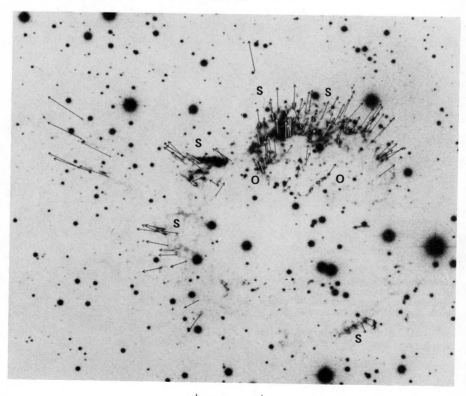

0   parsec   1

Some of the superdense core material survives. The ultimate fate of the remnant depends upon its mass. A remnant between about 0.1 and 1.4 solar masses will continue to collapse to a density of about 10^{15} g/cm³, at which point the neutrons generated by the interactions just mentioned will form a degenerate gas, analogous to the degenerate electron gas of Fig. 6-16; the pressure of this gas halts collape and preserves the remnant thereafter in the form of a *neutron star*. Radio astronomy has detected *pulsars* that have all the properties expected of rapidly rotating neutron stars.

Neutron degeneracy is not adequate to halt the collapse of remnants larger than about 1.4 solar masses. These continue to fall together into the twilight world of *black holes*, masses whose relationship to our universe is ambiguous. Black holes are so dense that the escape velocity (Eq. (2-4)) from their surfaces is greater than the speed of light. We can have no direct knowledge of their existence, because there is no way radiative energy emitted or reflected from them can escape to reach us.

ORIGIN OF THE CHEMICAL ELEMENTS

The pattern of elemental abundances inherited by the stars, the sun, and the planets from the gas and dust of interstellar space is understood to have been established by nuclear transmutations that occurred in stellar interiors and supernovas. Thus a substantial component of the interstellar gas and dust is thought to have resided in previous generations of stars, from which it was ejected into interstellar space.

The identity of a chemical element is established by the number of protons in its nucleus. All elements except hydrogen also contain neutrons in their nuclei. The number of protons (Z) plus neutrons (N) establishes the mass number (A) of a given nucleus. Each possible combination of Z and N is referred to as a *nuclide*. Nuclides having the same Z but different values of N are the *isotopes* of the element with atomic number Z.

The total inventory of nuclides in the solar system (i.e., all naturally occurring nuclides that are stable or that are radioactive with long half-lives) is shown in Fig. 6-19. These nuclides comprise 83 chemical elements. The mean abundances of the elements in the solar system are shown in Table 6-2. The values given are based on abundances in the solar atmosphere and in Cl carbonaceous chondrites (which are very similar to one another, Fig. 5-8, and thought to represent undifferentiated solar system material). Spectral studies show that ~ 95 percent of the stars in the galaxy have similar abundance patterns.

Several different processes of nucleosynthesis, which operate at different times and places in stars, are believed to give rise to the various nuclides in Fig. 6-19.

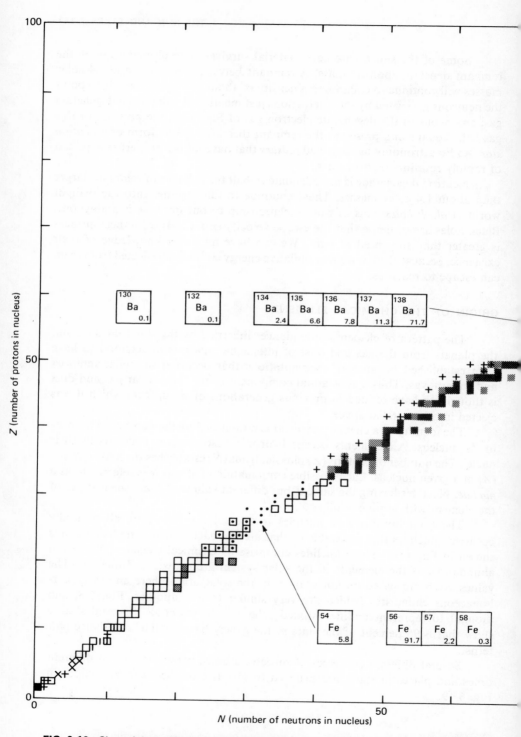

FIG. 6-19 Chart of the nuclides, showing all naturally occurring stable and long-lived radioactive nuclides. Symbols denote the probable mode(s) of origin of each nuclide. Enlargements are shown

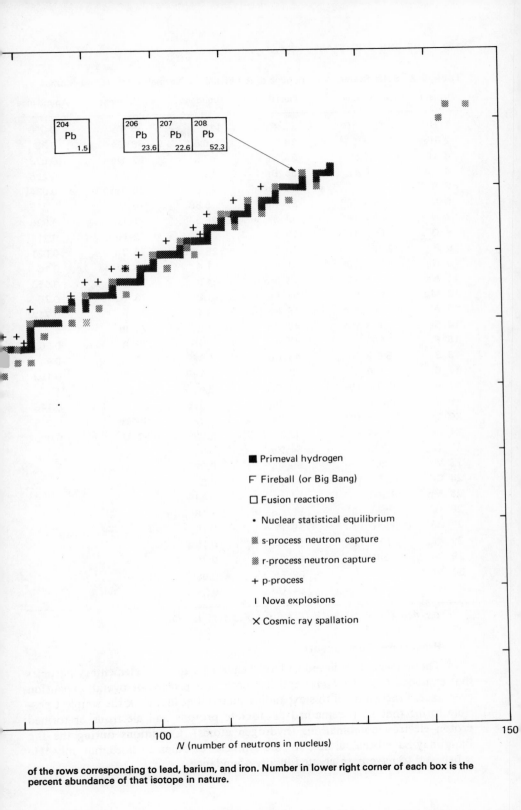

204 Pb			206 Pb	207 Pb	208 Pb
1.5			23.6	22.6	52.3

■ Primeval hydrogen

F Fireball (or Big Bang)

□ Fusion reactions

· Nuclear statistical equilibrium

▧ s-process neutron capture

▨ r-process neutron capture

+ p-process

I Nova explosions

X Cosmic ray spallation

100

150

N (number of neutrons in nucleus)

of the rows corresponding to lead, barium, and iron. Number in lower right corner of each box is the percent abundance of that isotope in nature.

Table 6-2 Solar System Abundances of the Elements, Normalized to 10^6 Si Atoms

Element	Abundance	Element	Abundance	Element	Abundance
1 H	3.18×10^{10}	32 Ge	115	65 Tb	0.055
2 He	2.21×10^9	33 As	6.6	66 Dy	0.36
3 Li	49.5	34 Se	67.2	67 Ho	0.079
4 Be	0.81	35 Br	13.5	68 Er	0.225
5 B	350	36 Kr	46.8	69 Tm	0.034
6 C	1.18×10^7	37 Rb	5.88	70 Yb	0.216
7 N	3.74×10^6	38 Sr	26.9	71 Lu	0.036
8 O	2.15×10^7	39 Y	4.8	72 Hf	0.21
9 F	2,450	40 Zr	28	73 Ta	0.021
10 Ne	3.44×10^6	41 Nb	1.4	74 W	0.16
11 Na	6.0×10^4	42 Mo	4.0	75 Re	0.053
12 Mg	1.061×10^6	44 Ru	1.9	76 Os	0.75
13 Al	8.5×10^4	45 Rh	0.4	77 Ir	0.717
14 Si	1.00×10^6	46 Pd	1.3	78 Pt	1.4
15 P	9,600	47 Ag	0.45	79 Au	0.202
16 S	5.0×10^5	48 Cd	1.48	80 Hg	0.4
17 Cl	5,700	49 In	0.189	81 Tl	0.192
18 Ar	1.172×10^5	50 Sn	3.6	82 Pb	4
19 K	4,200	51 Sb	0.316	83 Bi	0.143
20 Ca	7.21×10^4	52 Te	6.42	90 Th	0.058
21 Sc	35	53 I	1.09	92 U	0.0262
22 Ti	2,775	54 Xe	5.38		
23 V	262	55 Cs	0.387		
24 Cr	1.27×10^4	56 Ba	4.8		
25 Mn	9,300	57 La	0.445		
26 Fe	8.3×10^5	58 Ce	1.18		
27 Co	2,210	59 Pr	0.149		
28 Ni	4.80×10^4	60 Nd	0.78		
29 Cu	540	62 Sm	0.226		
30 Zn	1,244	63 Eu	0.085		
31 Ga	48	64 Gd	0.297		

Data from A. G. W. Cameron, Space Sci. Rev., *v. 15, 1973, 121–146.*

Pregalactic Components

The universe is believed to have begun as a mass of elementary particles that exploded (the *Big Bang*) and has been in a process of overall expansion ever since. Practically all this expanding material at first took the simplest possible form; that is, it remained as discrete protons and electrons or formed proton–electron combinations (hydrogen atoms). Conditions during the Big Bang may have been suitable for the synthesis of other nuclides, but only ^{4}He is believed to have been created in any abundance.

Fusion Reactions

Most of the other nuclides lighter than iron are understood to be the "ashes" of nuclear fusion reactions in stars that predated the solar system, as discussed above (Table 6-1). These nuclides were recycled to the interstellar medium by various types of stellar outbursts: planetary nebulae, supernovae, and novae. (Novae are small stellar explosions that shed only $\sim 10^{-5}$ of the mass of a star, and leave the star in an essentially unchanged state.)

Nuclear Statistical Equilibrium

Fusion reactions between nuclei cannot create nuclides heavier than the Fe-group elements (V, Cr, Mn, Fe, Co, Ni), because the resultant nuclei would be in a higher energy state and less stable than the nuclei that reacted to form them. When increasing temperature at the core of a star brings the chain of nuclear fusion reactions to this dead end, disintegrative as well as constructive reactions begin to occur. An equilibrium is reached between buildups and breakdowns, and this is believed to be reflected in the abundances of Fe-group nuclides.

Neutron Capture

Most nuclides heavier than the Fe-group are understood to be formed by neutron capture on Fe-group *seed nuclei*. When successive neutron captures make the value of N/Z too high in a nucleus, it tends to beta decay (i.e., it emits an electron, and one neutron is effectively transformed to a proton). Successive neutron captures and beta decays move nuclei to higher and higher mass numbers; the path they follow is marked by the positions of nuclides heavier than $Z \simeq 26$ in Fig. 6-19.

Actually, two tracks of neutron addition have been followed (Fig. 6-20). Neutrons that are generated during He-burning in stellar interiors can be added to Fe-group seed nuclei in a slow and orderly way (the *s-process*): slowly enough, that is, for nuclei to beta decay after each neutron addition, if they are unstable, before another neutron is added. (Note that the hypothetical He-burning stars must have inherited Fe-group seed nuclei from the interstellar medium, hence from nucleosynthetic activity in some even earlier generation of stars.) Neutrons are thought to be added very much more rapidly (the *r-process*), on the other hand, during the 1 to 100 sec of peak temperature during supernova explosions. Nuclides formed by this process follow a second, neutron-rich track beneath the pattern of nuclides in Fig. 6-19. This exists only momentarily, however; the neutron-rich nuclides are highly unstable, and undergo successive beta decays until stability is attained. In many cases, stable nuclides are formed that could not have been created by the s-process.

The p-Process

Nuclides on the proton-rich side of the s-process nuclides are thought to be created in supernovae either (1) by addition of protons to s-process nuclides, followed by positron emission or electron capture (which has the practical effect

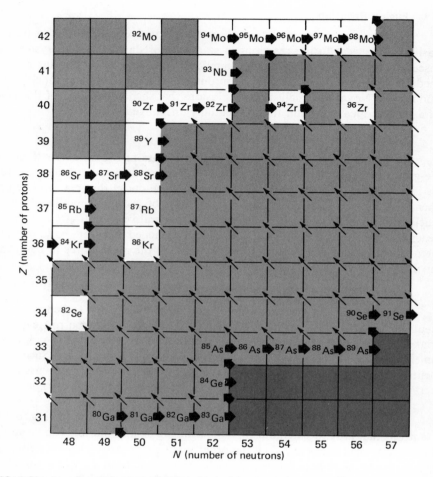

FIG. 6-20 A portion of the chart of the nuclides, showing the two paths of neutron addition that are thought to create heavy nuclides. Every box represents a possible nuclide, but most are unstable; only the nuclides in white boxes are stable (or, in a few cases, radioactive with very long half-lives). Most nuclides in the light gray boxes tend to beta decay (which shifts them to the next box upward and to the left; arrows) with half-lives of hours, minutes, or seconds. The nuclides in dark gray boxes beta decay even more rapidly than this. A portion of the *s-process track* is indicated by the upper chain of heavy arrows. This is followed when neutrons are added to a nucleus at a slow rate. Neutron additions move the nucleus rightward until it is transformed to a short-lived neutron-rich nuclide, whereupon it beta decays upward and to the left, becoming an isotope of a different chemical element than it had been. The nucleus can then capture additional neutrons until it beta decays again, and so forth. A portion of the *r-process track* appears at the bottom of the figure. When neutrons are added at a rate rapid compared with the half-lives of nuclides in the light gray boxes, as during a supernova explosion, the labeled chain of unstable neutron-rich nuclides is created. When neutron addition moves a nucleus into one of the dark gray boxes, it beta decays on a time scale even shorter than the duration of the supernova event, shifting the nuclide upward and to the left in the diagram. When the supernova neutron addition ends, the unstable nuclides left along the r-process track quickly beta decay (small arrows) until they become stable nuclides (white boxes). Many of these stable nuclides are also produced by the s-process, but some (e.g., ^{82}Se, ^{86}Kr, ^{87}Rb, ^{96}Zr) can be reached only by the r-process.

of converting newly added protons into neutrons) to form new stable nuclides, or (2) by photodisintegration reactions, whereby gamma rays eject neutrons from s-process nuclides.

Other Processes

The light nuclides ^6Li, ^9Be, ^{10}B, and ^{11}B, which are unstable in stellar interiors, are thought to be created by the action of cosmic rays on carbon, nitrogen, and oxygen atoms in interstellar space. The high-energy interaction of a cosmic-ray particle with a nucleus can fragment the latter into lighter nuclei, such as these.

Nova explosions may involve a momentary environment of high temperatures and abundant protons, which would create certain other of the light nuclides (e.g., ^{15}N).

While these processes of nucleosynthesis appear to have contributed to the elemental makeup of the great majority of stars in the disk of our galaxy, there is a class of stars whose spectra reveal an extremely low content of elements heavier than helium. These are old stars, and are believed to be first-generation members of the galaxy that did not have the opportunity to inherit heavy-element-enriched material from still older stars. The metal-poor stars follow eccentric, inclined orbits about the galactic center (Fig. 6-21), and thus spend most of their time in the galactic halo, above or below the galactic disk.

FIG. 6-21 Schematic cross section of the galaxy, showing the distribution of stellar populations. Population I stars, in the galactic disk, are metal-rich; the sun is an example. Population II stars, whose orbits about the galactic center carry them into the spherical galactic halo, are metal poor. A representative population II orbit is sketched.

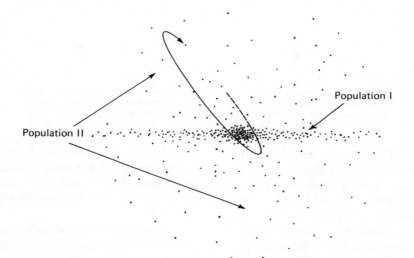

INTERSTELLAR GAS AND DUST

This section reviews the actual physical nature of the interstellar medium, before we discuss the transformation of one particular cloud of gas and dust into the sun and planets (Chapter 7). Spectral studies over a wide range of wavelengths inform us of the properties of the interstellar medium. The interstellar dust absorbs and scatters starlight in its passage through space. The shorter the wavelength, the stronger the extinction; so the net effect of interstellar dust is to filter out blue and violet wavelengths and "redden" the starlight that telescopes see. At infrared wavelengths actual absorption lines appear (e.g., Fig. 6-22), which tell something about the mineralogy of the dust grains.

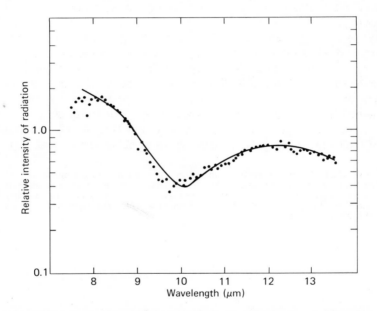

FIG. 6-22 Intensity of starlight in the infrared, after passage through interstellar dust (points); compared with the absorption spectrum of an amorphous magnesium silicate material synthesized in the laboratory (solid curve). After K. L. Day, *Astrophys. J. Letters*, v. 192, 1974, L15–L17.

The composition of the interstellar gas can be read from the absorption lines that the gas atoms superimpose on stellar spectra. Interstellar molecules, including compounds as complex as formaldehyde (H_2CO) and ethyl alcohol (C_2H_5OH), produce spectral emission lines in the centimeter wavelength range, detectable by radio telescopes.

These observations indicate that about 5 percent of the galaxy's mass is in the interstellar medium, and the mass ratio of gas to dust in interstellar space is ~100/1. The gas is mostly hydrogen and helium. It is depleted in metallic elements and carbon, nitrogen, and oxygen relative to the solar composition, suggesting that these "condensable" elements reside mostly in the dust grains. The average gas density in interstellar space is approximately one atom per cm^3.

Spectra of the interstellar dust indicate the presence of graphite, magnesium silicate, and water ice. Additional likely components are SiC, Fe_3O_4, and metallic iron. The grains of interstellar dust are believed to consist of mineral cores (~ 0.1 μm in diameter) surrounded by mantles of dirty ice (~ 0.3 μm in diameter); this configuration best accounts for the attenuating effect of the interstellar dust on starlight.

Starlight is somewhat polarized by the interstellar medium. This is believed to mean that the light is filtered through clouds of platey or rod-like mineral grains that are systematically aligned to some degree (polarizing sunglasses work in a similar fashion). The action of the galactic magnetic field on interstellar Fe_3O_4 (magnetite) crystals having plate-like shapes would probably produce the required alignment.

How did the interstellar mineral grains form? Probably not by condensation in interstellar space. There the density of atoms is so low that nucleation of the grains would be very unlikely. Furthermore, if condensation did occur at the extremely low temperatures of interstellar space ($\sim 20°$K for dust grains), it would be unselective. Any type of atom except hydrogen or helium striking a dust grain should stick, resulting in grains of mixed composition, whereas the spectrographic evidence indicates that interstellar grains consist of discrete minerals having particular compositions.

Instead, the interstellar grains are thought to have formed under circumstances of higher temperature and gas density in the atmospheres or neighborhoods of evolving stars. The solar winds emitted by red giant stars constitute a particularly favorable environment for dust condensation. The presence of dust can actually be inferred from the spectra of some red giants. Once condensed, the grains would be "blown" into interstellar space by light pressure and the stellar winds of their parent stars. In the case of stars of normal composition, the minerals expected to condense would be refractory Ca,Al-rich compounds, Mg silicates, and Fe metal. The relatively rare *carbon stars* would condense graphite and SiC.

There is one other potential source of interstellar dust grains. In Chapter 7, the condensation of mineral grains in the solar nebula will be discussed. The planets and meteorites are understood to have accreted from these nebular minerals, but the process may have been quite inefficient and wasteful, such that a large proportion of the mineral grains condensed were lost to interstellar space. The loss of nebular condensates from young stellar systems may have contributed a major proportion of the dust in interstellar space.

We have seen that there is a continual cycling of material between stars and interstellar space (Fig. 6-23). In addition to its cyclic character, however, it is important also to recognize the irreversible aspects of galactic evolution.

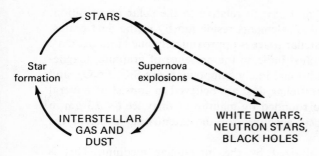

FIG. 6-23 Scheme of galactic evolution.

Element synthesis is steadily increasing the proportion of heavy elements in the substance of the galaxy; and, material is constantly being taken out of circulation, permanently locked up in superdense stellar objects.

seven
origin of the planets

References throughout this book have indicated that all questions will be answered in Chapter 7. The wary reader will understand it is not possible to really deliver on this; most aspects of solar-system origin are still poorly understood. Instead of setting forth a monolithic (but perishable) model for the origin of the solar system, this chapter will attempt to establish a broad framework of agreement about earliest events, identify the major questions within this framework, and explore alternative answers to the questions.

THE PRIMORDIAL NEBULA

The planets are generally believed to have been generated as minor by-products of the formation of the sun. Star formation has been discussed in Chapter 6, but with one important ingredient left out: rotation. It is expected that the cloud of interstellar gas and dust that gave rise to the sun (and other stars) would have been turbulent; when the cloud fragmented during contraction, individual fragments would be left turning this way and that, each having inherited the angular momentum of one or a few discrete whorls or eddies in the original cloud. Each cloud fragment (a potential star) would have rotated faster and faster as it further contracted, owing to conservation of its angular momentum. (The approximate relationship

$$h = I\omega = kr^2\omega$$

would hold for each fragment, where h is the angular momentum, I the moment of inertia, ω the angular velocity, r the radius of the fragment, and k a constant.

Since h remains constant, a decrease in r must be offset by an increase in ω.) As their rotational velocities increased, the fragments would have taken on more or less spun-out, disk-like forms. The configuration each fragment adopted as it approached solar-system dimensions would have depended on the amount of angular momentum it inherited from the original turbulent interstellar cloud, and this must have varied considerably from one fragment to another.

A fragment endowed with very little angular momentum must follow very nearly the simple process of contraction sketched in Chapter 6, with early- and late-arriving gas and dust adding to the growth of a rotating central condensation or protostar. The more angular momentum the fragment had, however, the more difficulty some components of it would have in joining the central condensation. As material from the faster-moving outer reaches of the rotating fragment was drawn toward the rotation axis, where the central condensation was forming, the angular velocity of this material about the rotation axis would have increased (because of the angular momentum conservation effect noted above) until it began to experience centrifugal forces that counterbalanced the inward gravitational pull of the central condensation. It could not move closer in than this. Thus much of the substance of such a cloud fragment could not immediately join the central condensation, but would flatten into a disk of gas and dust (a *nebula*) that turned about it.

Modeling studies have suggested that the contraction of cloud fragments with even a modest amount of angular momentum would not at first produce a simple spherical protostar as the central condensation, but a doughnut-like ring of dense material. Subsequently, this would contract into a spherical protostar; or if the system contained very much angular momentum, it would break into two or even three protostars orbiting about their mutual center of mass (Fig. 7-1). These could be expected to evolve into a binary or multiple star system. In this light, it is interesting to ask how abundant binary stars are in the galaxy. This cannot be evaluated straightforwardly, because binary stars are not always distinguishable from solitary stars (if they are very distant, for example, or if one of the pair is very dim). When allowance is made for the incompleteness of discovery of binaries, however, it appears likely that *most* of the stars in the galaxy are members of binary or multiple systems. This suggests that the solar system, which contains only one star, formed from a cloud fragment that had a less-than-average endowment of angular momentum. Presumably, this fragment evolved by contraction into a protosun surrounded by a flattened gaseous nebula, inside which dust and ice particles ultimately aggregated to form the planets. Origin of the planets within such a disk-like volume has long been held responsible for the nearly coplanar arrangement of planetary orbits, and for the common direction of revolution of the planets about the sun. The existence of nebulas surrounding several very young stars has been inferred from their infrared spectra (Fig. 7-2).

There is a crucial uncertainty in the behavior of the nebula that defines two very different paths leading to planet formation. The question is whether or

FIG. 7-1 The character of a protostar–nebula system formed by contraction of a cloud fragment would depend upon the angular momentum of the latter. A fragment with little angular momentum would produce a large protostar and minor nebula (A). More angular momentum would produce a more spun-out system (B), in which the nebula has increased prominence. A very rapidly rotating cloud fragment would produce a binary or multiple protostar system upon contraction (C).

FIG. 7-2 Artist's impression of the luminous gas disk (nebula) that is thought to comprise MWC 349, a stellar object which emits strongly in the infrared. The disk-like form of the object cannot be resolved by a telescope, but is inferred from its spectral properties. The young central star is much more massive ($\sim 30 M_\odot$) than the sun ($1 M_\odot$); the disk is thought to contain $\sim 0.015 M_\odot$ of material. The brightness of the object has diminished by 88 percent in 39 yr of observation; this is attributed to rapid dissipation of its disk material. Figure courtesy of E. F. Erickson and the NASA Ames Research Center.

not the nebula would have maintained its integrity as a smoothly continuous disk. As discussed earlier, there is reason to think local self-gravitational effects would have caused the original interstellar cloud to fragment as it contracted. As the first large fragments contracted further, they would themselves divide into smaller fragments. The process would repeat as smaller and smaller hierarchies of contracting fragments were produced. Why should we assume that the process would cease when one of these fragments spun out to form the solar nebula? Wouldn't the nebula itself be unstable against fragmentation into discrete self-gravitating masses, each in orbit about the protosun?

The effect that would work against such a process is tidal disruption of the nebula fragments by the gravitational pull of the protosun at the center of the nebula. It is the presence of this massive central body that makes the nebula fundamentally different from the interstellar cloud fragment that preceded it. The Roche limit criterion of Eq. (4-2) is pertinent to the situation; it suggests the relationship between the mass density of a fragment (ρ), its distance from the protosun (d), and the mass of the latter (M) that has to be satisfied if the fragment is to resist tidal disruption. This reduces to the observation that, if the protosun is massive and the nebula thin, nebular fragmentation could not occur and the nebula would remain smoothly integral. If the nebula is substantial in

FIG. 7-3 Fragmentation of hypothetical, relatively massive nebula into gaseous protoplanets (Schematic! Don't count the protoplanets.)

mass compared to the protosun, it will tend to divide into fragments or protoplanets that are stable against tidal disruption (Fig. 7-3). As we have seen, the relative masses of protosun and nebula probably depend rather directly on the amount of angular momentum that the solar system's cloud fragment inherited.

If the nebula divided into gaseous protoplanets, each with its own gravitational field, solid particles within each protoplanet may have tended to settle to its center, there to form a dense accretion or *planetesimal*. Many such planetesimals could have ultimately joined to form the planets of the solar system. (The number of protoplanets initially formed may have been much larger than the present number of planets.) If the gaseous nebula was stable against fragmentation, on the other hand, we must suppose that solid particles accreted at large within it, forming planetesimals and finally planets. Neither of these possibilities can be excluded; but since practically all meteorite and planetology research in recent years has been interpreted in the latter framework, the present chapter will concentrate on the proposition that planets were formed by at-large accretion of solid particles within the nebula.

Processing of Dust in the Nebula

Our conception of physical conditions in the nebula, based on astrophysical modeling, has changed in recent years. Previously, it was thought that the inner portion of the nebula (the region where the terrestrial planets and asteroids were to form) was very hot for a time, so that any interstellar mineral grains in that region would have been vaporized and, upon subsequent cooling

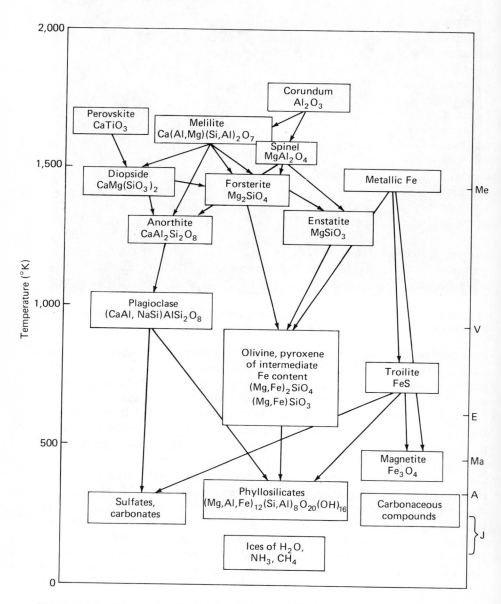

FIG. 7-4 The sequence of condensation of minerals (simplified) from a nebula of solar composition. Arrows denote continued reaction with the nebular gases, transforming the mineral in the upper box into those in lower boxes. If the minerals remain dispersed in the nebula until very low temperatures are reached and complete equilibrium is maintained, only the materials in the lower boxes should be available for accretion (C1 carbonaceous chondrites). The presence of higher-temperature minerals in other chondrite types reflects incomplete equilibration during cooling, and/or accretion at temperatures greater than 500°K. Temperatures at which the terrestrial planets, asteroids, and satellites of Jupiter (J) are held to have accreted, according to the Equilibrium Condensation Model, are indicated on the right edge of the diagram.

of the gas, recondensed. Now it appears that compression of the nebular gases during their contraction would not have developed high enough temperatures to accomplish this. There is no obvious reason why interstellar grains would have been vaporized, except perhaps very close in to the protosun (inside the present orbit of Mercury).

Direct evidence of what *did* go on in the nebula is believed to be displayed by the chondritic meteorites, which are generally held to be surviving samples of aggregated particulate matter from the nebula. Suppose that the nebular gases *had* been heated to the point that included mineral grains were vaporized; we can, using the principles of thermodynamics, calculate the sequence of minerals that would condense from these gases as they cooled (Fig. 7-4). It turns out that the carbonaceous chondrites contain inclusions (Fig. 5-4(B)) consisting of minerals that correspond very closely to those appearing at highest temperatures in the nebular condensation sequence. Often these minerals occur in the chondritic Ca,Al-rich inclusions in layers or shells such that lower-temperature minerals overlie and enclose higher-temperature minerals. This demonstrates with considerable certainty that at least some components of chondritic meteorites formed by condensation from nebular or solar gases that had somehow been made very hot.

On the other hand, there is some evidence that the nebula at large was not heated to such an extent that interstellar grains in it were wholly vaporized. If this had occurred, and the vapors in the nebula were well mixed, we can expect that the isotopic compositions of the various elements in the gas would be homogenized. However, studies of the isotopic composition of oxygen in individual Ca,Al-rich inclusions and chondrules separated from carbonaceous chondrites show that these consist of mixtures of materials having two fundamentally different types of oxygen (Fig. 7-5). Radioactive decay has nothing to do with this anomaly; none of the oxygen isotopes are radioactive daughters. Presumably, the two types of oxygen derive from two different astrophysical environments that contributed to the interstellar cloud that gave rise to the solar system. In any case, they were never completely mixed in the nebula. One interpretation that can be placed on this is that at least some of the interstellar grains in the nebula were never vaporized. If they had been, their oxygen would have mingled with that of the nebular gases, and its special identity would be lost. Presumably, these unvaporized interstellar grains were incorporated in varying proportions in the chondrules and inclusions of the carbonaceous chondrites. (Another interpretation, however, would be that the nebula was initially isotopically heterogeneous from one side to the other, and vaporization and recondensation happened before the nebular gases could mix thoroughly. Chondrites could then end up incorporating some condensate particles from the high-^{16}O side of the nebula, and some from the low-^{16}O side.)

Chondrules as well as Ca,Al-rich inclusions have incorporated exotic high-^{16}O oxygen, suggesting a common mode of origin, presumably condensation from a cooling vapor. The minerals that comprise chondrules appear in

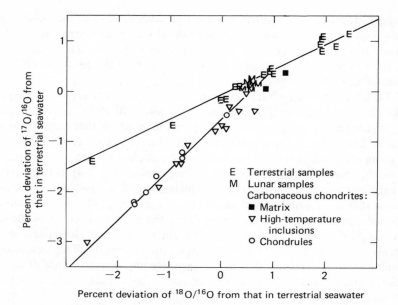

FIG. 7-5 Isotopic compositions of oxygen in terrestrial, lunar, and meteoritic materials. Some fractionation of oxygen isotopes occurs during any geochemical process (e.g., separation of crystals from a melt); the nature of these fractionations is understood, and is represented by the upper line in this plot. Differences in the composition of oxygen among terrestrial and lunar samples can be accounted for in this way. However, the components of carbonaceous chondrites display variability in oxygen composition (lower curve) that cannot be explained by geochemical fractionation processes. Instead, these samples are understood to represent mixtures in various proportions of two fundamentally different types of oxygen that entered the early solar system: a component similar to that in Earth and moon (upper end of the chondrite curve); and a component very much enriched in ^{16}O, which would plot somewhere far to the lower left of the chondrite curve. After R. N. Clayton et al., *Science,* v. 182, 1973, 485–488.

the middle range of temperatures (1,500° to 600°K) in the condensation sequence (Fig. 7-4). However, the once-liquid state of chondrules is difficult to reconcile with physical conditions in the nebula. At the low gas pressures (less than 0.01 atm) thought reasonable for the nebula, condensation of the chondrule minerals would occur at such low temperatures that solid mineral grains, not liquid droplets, would be the product. Several modes of origin have been proposed for these objects. (1) Condensation may have produced supercooled liquid droplets rather than the equilibrium product, solid crystals. (2) Gas–dust fractionations may have occurred in the nebula, along with unspecified high-energy enents that caused localized vaporization of dust and recondensation. In dust-enriched regions, the hot gas would have metal concentrations higher than those in solar gas. Condensation in such an enriched system occurs at higher temperatures, possibly in the melting range. (3) Condensation of chondrules may have occurred in gaseous protoplanets, where pressures would be relatively high. (4) The chondrules may have nothing to do with condensation; a widely held view is that they are chilled splash droplets from high-energy impacts on planetary surfaces or between small objects in space. Whatever the process, it appears to thave worked efficiently and pervasively at the time when the chondritic meteorites were being aggregated, since chondrules are very abundant in these meteorites, in some cases comprising over 70 percent of their volume (Fig. 7-6).

We are left with this dilemma: chondrites contain high-temperature minerals, some or all of which were produced by condensation from hot nebular gases; but it is unclear what agency heated the nebula to the required temperatures. Wholesale compression of the gases during formation of the nebula does not seem adequate, nor does radiative heating by the protosun, since the region of the nebula where the asteroids (the presumed source of chondrites) formed was far removed from the protosun and the intervening nebular gases would have been opaque to short-wavelength radiation.

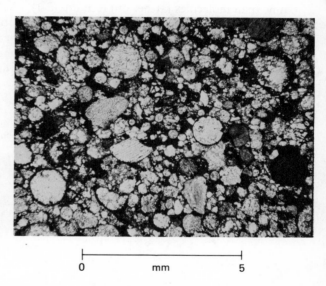

FIG. 7-6 Thin section of the Tieschitz (Czechoslovakia) chondrite, showing abundant chondrules and chondrule fragments embedded in a dark fine-grained matrix. From J. A. Wood, *Meteorites and the Origin of Planets* (New York: McGraw-Hill, 1968), 117 pp.

```
0            mm            5
```

There are indications that the heating of the nebula was localized and transitory. The various chondrite types contain different and characteristic populations of chondrules and inclusions, suggesting that each chondrite type was produced by a local high-energy event which generated that particular condensate population; and that accretion into chondritic planetesimals followed promptly, before there was time for mixing of the condensates from many high-energy events to occur in the nebula. The preservation of glass in many chondrules and the generally nonequilibrium character of mineral assemblages in many chondrites demonstrate that cooling of their environments was rapid. Slow cooling would have permitted the glass to crystallize and the minerals to react to equilibrium.

The nature of the hypothetical high-energy events is not known. One possibility might be compressive heating of gases within gaseous protoplanets of the type mentioned earlier, followed by tidal disruption of the individual protoplanets. Another is the shock compression produced by late-arriving, more or less discrete masses of gas and dust from the solar system's cloud fragment, as each of these fell into the surface of the nebula.

Motions of the Nebula

While these thermal and chemical events were occurring in the nebula, there were also mass motions in it (Fig. 7-7) that ultimately led to its disappearance. Consider the following two ways that the nebula might be in motion about the sun. First, if each gas molecule was completely independent of other molecules in the nebula, we could picture it simply orbiting the protosun like a tiny planet. The innermost molecules would circuit the protosun in a shorter time than molecules farther out (see Eq. (2-1), relating the period of a planet to its mean distance), so there would be shearing motion everywhere in the nebula, with any given volume of gas pulling ahead of the next-farther-out volume and lagging behind the next-farther-in volume. Second, if the gas molecules were somehow tied to one another, we could picture the nebula rotating like a rigid disk or wheel.

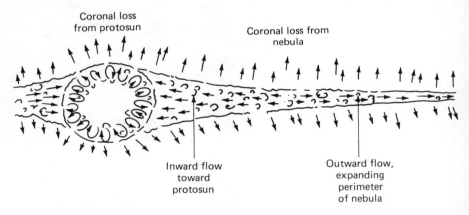

FIG. 7-7 Gas motions in and away from primordial protosun and nebula (schematic).

The actual behavior of the nebula would have been somewhere between these two extremes; closest to the first case described, but with an element of viscosity added, which meant the gas molecules were not completely independent of each other. So although there would be shearing motion in the nebula as described in the first case, volumes of gas would not be quite as free to pass one another or lag behind as in the case of independently orbiting objects. Consequently, the inner part of the nebula would be made to turn rather more slowly, and the outer part more rapidly, than would be appropriate for independent objects orbiting at those distances from the protosun. But this is a dynamically unstable situation: if an orbiting body (or volume of gas) has less than the circular orbital velocity at a given distance from the attracting center, it must adopt an orbit that carries it in closer to the latter. Conversely, if it moves at greater than the circular orbital velocity, it adopts an orbit that carries it farther out from the attracting center. The net effect on the nebula of the tendencies described would have been to spin it thinner and thinner, with gas from the inner nebula migrating farther inward, much of it ultimately joining the protosun; while gas from the outer part of the disk moved farther and farther out, until the nebula took on a diameter vastly larger than the present solar system.

Superimposed on these organized motions of the nebular gases would have been turbulence. In addition, the protosun may have reached an evolutionary stage in which its outer layers were in vigorous convective motion. In Chapter 6 we noted that mechanical motions of this type near the surface of the present sun translate upward into the solar corona, a thin, very hot, ionized medium (plasma) that streams away from the sun. Our expectation is that similar but more vigorous motions in the nebula and protosun after the infall of interstellar cloud material was completed would have developed a massive corona surrounding that primitive system, which would cause plasma to be lost to space at a much greater rate than the solar wind is currently carrying it away from the sun.

A large fraction of the nebular gas may have been dissipated by coronal streaming from the surfaces of the nebula. After the nebula had diminished in size, plasma streaming from the protosun was probably influential in sweeping the remainder of it (the nebula) away. (The T Tauri class of stars, which are at this stage of evolution and are observed to be shedding plasma at a rate 10^8 to 10^9 times greater than that of the present solar wind, appear to be in the process of dispersing surrounding opaque clouds.) Remaining small dust grains as well as gas would be blown away at this time by the early intense solar wind.

ORIGIN OF THE TERRESTRIAL PLANETS

Planetary accretion, like most other aspects of solar system origin, is imperfectly understood. Once planetary nuclei (objects some tens of kilometers in dimension, say) had gotten started, it is easy enough to see how they would grow by sweeping up smaller particles. But it has always been difficult to see how the start was made; why dust particles, chondrules, and Ca,Al-rich inclusions chose to clump together.

The idea of gaseous protoplanets, mentioned earlier, provides one explanation. Solid particles would settle to the center of each of these nebular fragments, there to form a planetary nucleus that would survive after the gaseous envelope of the protoplanet was dissipated. There is also a way in which planetary nucleation might have gotten started in the nebula at large. This depends upon the settling of solid particles toward the midplane of the nebula (Fig. 7-8), drawn there by gravitational attraction. Only relatively coarse particles—chon-

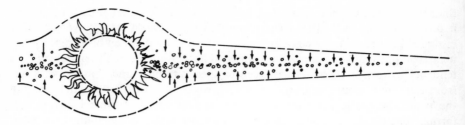

FIG. 7-8 Motion of solid particles, drawn by gravitational attraction of the nebula and protosun toward the midplane of the nebula (schematic).

drules, Ca, Al-rich inclusions, clumps of dust—could settle; finely dispersed dust would be kept churned up in the nebula by gas turbulence.

Once a dense concentration of solid particles accumulated near the midplane of the nebula, there would be a tendency for the dust disk to become gravitationally unstable, separating and coagulating into aggregations of a few kilometers dimension, which would then serve as accretion nuclei. The gravitational instability alluded to is analogous to that discussed earlier for the overall nebula, but in this case only solid particles are involved, which attract one another independently of the gas that they are embedded in.

We expect that the planetary nuclei, or planetesimals, had a character similar to that of chondritic meteorites at this point. It may even be possible to understand the differences between chondrite types in terms of midplane settling. Far out in the nebula, where the gas temperature was intrinsically low, the formation of "sticky" carbonaceous compounds (Fig. 7-4) and possibly even ice crystals (snowflakes) may have acted to bond dust grains of low-temperature mineralogy into lumps large enough to settle to the midplane, where they coagulated into planetesimals of carbonaceous chondrite composition. Perhaps temperatures in the inner nebula were too high to permit formation of these dust-bonding agents, and the only objects coarse enough to move to the midplane were chondrules and Ca,Al-rich inclusions that had been melted or vaporized and then recondensed by high-energy events. Coagulations of this material would more nearly resemble ordinary chondrites.

Once a set of planetary nuclei was established in this or some other fashion, they would have continued to sweep up stray particulate matter and merge with one another, growing to asteroidal dimensions (hundreds of kilometers). Because the planetesimals and particulate matter moved in nearly circular and therefore very similar orbits, relative velocities would have been small. Impacts would have been cushioned by unconsolidated regoliths that accumulated on the planetesimal surfaces (many of the meteorites have properties characteristic of soil breccias), so encounters were probably more often constructive or acquisitive than disruptive. Asteroidal dimensions would have been achieved in some thousands of years.

At about this time the character of the accumulation process is thought to have changed in an important way. In part this was because the gaseous nebula, which had acted to keep small objects channeled into circular orbits, was dissipated, leaving planetesimals and smaller aggregations orbiting in the vacuum of space. In part it was because some planetesimals had grown large enough to begin exerting a substantial gravitational influence on objects that passed near them.

This meant that during near encounters planetesimals tended to be perturbed out of their docile circular orbits and into more eccentric, inclined orbits, as suggested by Fig. 2-7. Orbits would have grown "wilder and wilder" with time, which means that relative velocities between planetesimals in intersecting orbits became greater. Higher impact velocities would have caused more disruptive collisions; a larger proportion of encounters resulted in dispersal of one or both objects, rather than net growth. In these circumstances only the largest bodies would have had potent enough gravitational fields to "hold down" most of the debris from high-velocity collisions, and grow with time. Smaller planetesimals would be systematically destroyed by collisions, their debris being eventually swept up by the larger objects or driven out of the solar system by light pressure.

Out of this chain of captures and collisions the terrestrial planets grew. Planetesimals often must have impacted the planets at glancing angles, and these asymmetric additions of material established the rotation rates and inclinations of the rotation axes of the planets (Table 2-1; Fig. 7-9). The present inclination of a planet's rotation axis can be used to estimate the size of the planetesimals that were joining it in the last stages of its assembly, in the sense that the glancing addition of one huge planetesimal could knock the rotation axis of a planet on its side (as is the case with Uranus), whereas the effects of many small planetesimals, each added asymmetrically, would tend to cancel one another out,

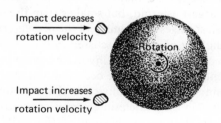

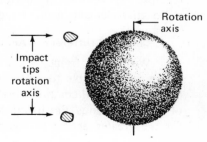

FIG. 7-9 Effects of off-center impacts by planetesimals on the rotation of a growing planet. Above, the planet is viewed from above (parallel to its rotation axis); below, the planet is viewed from the side (perpendicular to its rotation axis).

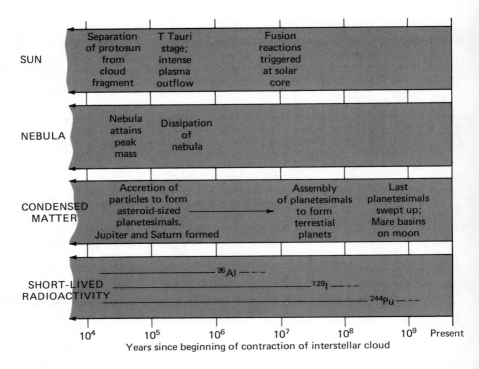

FIG. 7-10 Postulated time scale of major events in the early history of the solar system; logarithmic scale. Lines labeled "Short-lived Radioactivity" indicate that portion of solar system history when significant amounts of three important radionuclides were still undecayed.

leaving the planet's rotation axis nearly perpendicular to the ecliptic. It is estimated that the last major planetesimals joining Earth and Mars were larger than the largest asteroid, but smaller than the moon.

The last stages of assembly of the planets occurred over a period of $\sim 10^8$ yr. The chronology of events discussed in this chapter is summarized in Fig. 7-10. Our idea of the time scales involved comes partly from theoretical modeling of the events believed to have occurred, but also from evidence in the meteorites that certain short-lived radioactive elements were still "alive" when they were incorporated in the planetesimals (now asteroids) that the meteorites come from (Chapter 5). Bars at the bottom of Fig. 7-10 indicate the times when these radioactive elements would have decayed to undetectable levels.

Chemical Differences Among the Planets

Within the framework of coagulation, capture, and growth discussed above, is it possible to understand how the terrestrial planets came to have different chemical compositions? The reader will recall that the mean densities of Mercury, Venus, Earth, and Mars are different, even after allowance is made for the greater degree of compression of the interiors of the larger planets

(Table 4-1; recapitulated in Table 7-1). These density differences must reflect variations in the chemical makeup of the planets.

Table 7-1   Mean Uncompressed Mass
Densities of the Terrestrial
Planets

Planet	Density (g/cm³)
MERCURY	5.4
VENUS	~4.2
EARTH	~4.2
MARS	3.3
MOON	3.35

The chemical variability undoubtedly involves the element iron, which is the only abundant element that is substantially heavier than the other metallic elements, and which also can occur in a series of minerals having very different mass densities (Table 7-2). There are two possibilities; first, something might have acted to fractionate iron from the other elements during the formation of the planets in such a way that the farther from the sun a planet formed the less iron it received, so the smaller its net mass density was. Second, the abundance of iron relative to other metallic elements might be the same in all planets, but the state of oxidation of the iron varies among the planets. (Some metallic elements can exist in a series of chemical states in the planets, ranging from *reduced* to *oxidized*. The higher the degree of oxidation, the more atoms of oxygen or any other electronegative element the metallic element is combined with. The most highly oxidized state of iron is Fe^{3+}, which occurs in combination with oxygen in minerals such as hematite, Fe_2O_3. A less oxidized form of iron, Fe^{2+}, occurs in many minerals, such as olivine, $(Mg,Fe)_2SiO_4$, and troilite, FeS. The least oxidized (most reduced) form of iron, Fe^0, is the pure metal.)

Table 7-2   Oxidation State of Iron and Mass Density of Several Iron-Bearing Minerals

Mineral	Formula	Oxidation State	Mass Density (g/cm³)
METALLIC IRON	Fe	Fe^0	7.6
MAGNETITE	Fe_3O_4	Fe^{2+}, Fe^{3+}	5.2
TROILITE	FeS	Fe^{2+}	4.7
FAYALITE	Fe_2SiO_4	Fe^{2+}	4.4
GOETHITE	$Fe_2O_3 \cdot H_2O$	Fe^{3+}	4.3
FE-RICH CHLORITE	$(Fe, Mg, Al)_{12}(Si, Al)_8O_{20}(OH)_{16}$	Fe^{2+}	~3.3
HISINGERITE	$Fe_2O_3 \cdot 2SiO_2 \cdot nH_2O$	Fe^{3+}	~3.0

Perhaps the farther out from the sun a planet formed, the more highly oxidized its iron was. The minerals of oxidized iron tend to be less dense than those of reduced iron (Table 7-2).

Four principal models that address the chemistry of planet formation have been developed in recent years. These are discussed in turn, below.

Equilibrium Condensation Model

According to the Equilibrium Condensation Model, temperatures in the primordial nebula at the time when coagulation of planetesimals began were relatively high near the protosun ($\sim 1,400°$K at the present orbit of Mercury) and declined outward in the disk ($\sim 600°$K at Earth's orbit, $\sim 300°$K in the asteroid belt). Dust grains were in equilibrium with surrounding nebular gases, and had the compositions dictated by the condensation sequence (Fig. 7-4) for whatever temperature obtained at their particular position in the nebula. As Fig. 7-4 indicates, under these circumstances the mineralogy would be quite different at the positions of the various terrestrial planets. After accretion commenced, most dust grains would be buried inside planetesimals and no longer in reactive contact with nebular gases; so even if temperatures later declined in the nebula, the mineralogical combinations specified by Fig. 7-4 (and their net mass densities) would remain unchanged.

Specifically, according to this model, when the dust that was to form Mercury began to accrete and was isolated from the nebula, the latter was at about 1,400°K, at which point all calcium and aluminum were condensed into refractory compounds, all iron was condensed in the metallic (reduced) state, and some but not all magnesium and silicon were condensed as forsterite. The remaining magnesium and silicon were still at large as vapors in the nebula. The types of solid grains just named went to make up the planet Mercury. In this model the high mass density of that planet is due to both the abundance of iron (since magnesium and silicon, the other abundant elements, are incompletely condensed) and its oxidation state (i.e., totally reduced; metallic iron has the highest density of any form of iron).

Complete condensation of magnesium and silicon occurred in the region of Venus ($\sim 900°$K), so that planet has a lower metallic iron/silicates ratio than Mercury; but virtually all iron is still in the metallic state. Earth formed in a cooler region of the nebula ($\sim 600°$K), where iron would have been stable as grains of troilite (FeS), iron silicates, and iron metal. It would seem that the presence of relatively oxidized forms of iron, as compared with the totally reduced state of iron in Venus, would ensure that Earth's mean uncompressed density is substantially less than that of Venus; but sulfur is a relatively heavy element, having an atomic weight greater than that of the mean atomic weight of all the elements thought to comprise Earth, so the addition of a large quantity of this element could explain the fact that Earth appears to be slightly denser than Venus according to some internal modeling studies.

At Mars's position in the nebula ($\sim 450°$K), all iron was present as the

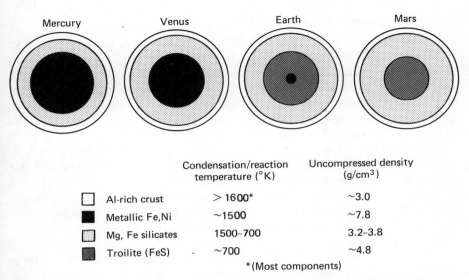

FIG. 7-11 Compositions and structures of the terrestrial planets (drawn to identical diameters), according to the Equilibrium Condensation Model. The Mg,Fe silicates are iron-poor in the case of Mercury and condensed at ~1,500°K; farther out in the solar system they reacted to progressively lower temperatures and contain more Fe^{2+}. In general, the lower-temperature mineral assemblages are less dense than high-temperature assemblages. After J. S. Lewis, Scientific American, v. 230, March 1974, 51–65.

sulfide or silicates; no iron metal was stable. Conditions in the asteroid belt were appropriate for the formation of carbonaceous chondrites. The overall mineralogical makeup of the terrestrial planets according to the Equilibrium Condensation Model is summarized in Fig. 7-11.

The Equilibrium Condensation Model is somewhat misleadingly labeled. It should be stressed that there is no requirement that interstellar dust grains in the nebula be vaporized so they can recondense through the condensation sequence; all that is required is for the dust to equilibrate according to the condensation diagram at one of the temperatures mentioned above. Near the present orbit of Mercury, equilibration might have entailed partial volatilization of the original interstellar dust grains, and no recondensation at all. The temperature range cited for formation of the terrestrial planets is relatively low, and can be equated with the range of ambient temperatures in astrophysically modeled nebulas; the high-temperature excursions that seem necessary to account for chondrules and inclusions in meteorites, discussed earlier in this chapter, are not a necessary element of the Equilibrium Condensation Model.

In this model, planetary accretion is postulated to be a relatively slow process, to avoid undue heating of the planetary materials and losses of the more volatile components. The accreting material is held to be relatively uniform in composition for each planet; the present internal heterogeneity of the planets developed later, when radioactive heating melted planetary interiors and permitted density separations to occur.

Heterogeneous Accretion Model

Although the Equilibrium Condensation Model accounts for the densities of the terrestrial planets in a satisfying way, some other properties of the planets contradict it. At the condensation temperatures indicated for Venus, Earth, and Mars, no hydrated minerals or carbonaceous compounds should be stable; this leaves the atmospheres of the planets and the hydrosphere and buried carbon of Earth unaccounted for. Also, the rocks of Earth's crust and upper mantle contain substantial amounts of iron in the Fe^{3+} state, as well as Fe^{2+}. This is not permitted by the condensation sequence at as high a temperature as $600°K$. Furthermore, iron in such a high state of oxidation would be unstable if it were ever in the presence of reduced, metallic iron, such as Earth's core contains; if the two forms of iron had ever been mingled, it seems they should have reacted to establish an intermediate oxidation state for all the iron. It does not seem possible that a single uniform raw material in Earth could have separated to form these two antipathetic fractions.

The Heterogeneous Accretion Model was designed to overcome these difficulties. In this model, interstellar grains were completely vaporized in the nebula; then, as condensation occurred, accretion took place with equal promptness, so there was a tendency to sweep up each mineral component in the condensation sequence as soon as it appeared, sequestering it in an accreting planet and preventing it from reacting further with the nebular gases. Clearly, this would give rise to layered planets, with the most refractory minerals near the core and the lower-temperature minerals near the surface of each planet.

Thus in the case of Earth (which this model most specifically addresses), at first a core of refractory Ca,Al-rich minerals accreted; then this was surrounded by a thick layer of early-condensed metallic nickel–iron; then a mantle of olivine and pyroxene accreted on top of this. Note that the core–mantle structure of Earth is ready-made, and does not depend on melting and gravity fractionation. The only difficulty is the placement of calcium and aluminum compounds at the center of Earth, instead of in its crust, where calcium and aluminum are now concentrated. However, the rapid rate of accretion postulated for Earth would have guaranteed that a large fraction of the energy of impact of accreting planetesimals was retained as heat, raising the temperature of the growing Earth to the melting range. Once Earth melted, low-density calcium- and aluminum-rich material originally at its center would have fractionated toward its surface. (Accretional melting of Earth can be avoided only if, after each impact, enough time elapses to allow radiative dissipation of most of the heat generated at the point of impact before the next impact affects that area.)

As nebular cooling, condensation, and accretion progressed, the point was finally reached where low-temperature, highly oxidized and hydrated solids—similar to those that comprise carbonaceous chondrites—condensed. These were accreted as a final veneer onto Earth, most of which was the product of much higher temperature processes. This low-temperature veneer is the source of the Fe^{3+}, water, carbon and other volatiles that are so evident at Earth's surface (and so vital to our existence). Note that the metallic iron of Earth's core and the Fe^{3+} of its crust never had to coexist; they come from different temperature regimes of the condensation sequence, and have always been separated by a 3,000-km-thick barrier, Earth's mantle.

A difficulty with this model comes from geophysical evidence which indicates that the core is not pure metallic iron and nickel, but that some lighter element is also present in substantial amounts (see Fig. 6-6 in S. P. Clark, Jr. *Structure of the Earth*); The light alloying element is generally thought to be sulfur, but the Heterogeneous Accretion Model prevents the formation of a sulfur-rich core by accreting and burying a pure-metal core before the temperature in the nebula falls to a low enough value to permit reaction of the metal with nebular gases to form troilite (FeS). Proponents of the Heterogeneous Accretion Model are forced to argue that the light alloying element in Earth's core is metallic (reduced) silicon, not sulfur.

In addition, the requirements for total vaporization and recondensation of dust in the nebula, and for accretion on a time scale as rapid as that of cooling and condensation in the nebula, are at odds with our present conception of the behavior of the nebula, as discussed earlier in this chapter.

Reduction During Accretion Model

In the Reduction During Accretion Model, Venus, Earth, and Mars are held to have accreted from a common type of material, which was at equilibrium with the nebula at low temperatures. This substance was identical or equivalent to Cl carbonaceous chondrites: it contained highly oxidized iron, carbonaceous compounds, hydrated mineral phases, and a full complement of volatile elements.

The accreting material was heated to varying degrees by the energy of impacts on growing planetary surfaces. While the planets were still small, the impacts were presumably at relatively low velocities, and the amount of heat generated was small. The bigger the planets grew, however, the more strongly their gravity attracted approaching planetestimals, and the more energetically the latter impacted them. A planet growing in this manner would develop a zoned thermal structure at the outset: it would be relatively cold at the center with temperatures increasing toward the surface. Temperatures in the outer reaches of an accreting Earth could be high enough to melt and even boil those levels of the planet.

Where this happened, carbon in the accreting material tended to reduce the oxidized iron, producing metallic iron (needed for Earth's core) and CO_2 or CO (which was outgassed):

$$Fe_3O_4 + 2C \longrightarrow 3Fe + 2CO_2 \tag{7-1}$$

Volatile elements were vaporized and swept out of the upper levels of Earth along with CO_2 and H_2O. As these components were emitted from Earth's surface, they were swept away by surrounding nebular gases or the early intense T Tauri solar wind and lost from Earth altogether. (Note, however, that the estimated time scales of accretion and nebular dissipation, Fig. 7-10, do not appear to allow this.)

This model produces an Earth with abundant metallic iron from which to form a core, and some unheated planetesimal material to serve as a source of the Fe^{3+}, carbon, water and other volatiles that occur near the surface of the present Earth. However, these components are in the wrong places at the outset; it must be postulated that molten metallic iron and FeS sank to the center of Earth, and cool unreduced material rose from the center to the surface of Earth, without the two substances mingling and equilibrating with one another.

This model explains the differences in uncompressed densities among the planets as being a simple consequence of their sizes. Earth, the largest, attracted planetesimals the most strongly during the last stages of accretion; hence it was the most severely heated, its oxidized iron was the most completely reduced to metal, and so it has the highest mass density (apart from Mercury). Venus and Mars, progressively smaller planets, were less reduced and have lower densities.

Mercury, small but very dense, has to be an exception. Even complete reduction of the iron in Cl chondrite material would not produce a planet as dense as Mercury. It is postulated that the Equilibrium Condensation process (above) did affect this one planet, delivering more metallic iron and less silicates to it than to the other terrestrial planets.

Nonequilibrium Components Model

The Nonequilibrium Components Model holds that the terrestrial planets (or more properly the planetesimals that preceded them) accreted from the same type of particulate matter that formed the chondritic meteorites. Most unmetamorphosed chondrites do not consist wholly of mineral grains that equilibrated at one nebular temperature, such as the raw materials for the planets are assumed to be in all three models discussed above. Instead, these chondrites usually contain a disequilibrium mixture of components representing different temperatures of formation in the nebula, ranging from high-temperature Ca,Al-rich inclusions to low-temperature, fine-grained, highly oxidized matrix. Included are minerals containing iron in all possible states of oxidation.

Using this very accommodating form of raw material, it is possible to imagine a mode of formation of the terrestrial planets that incorporates elements of all three previously discussed models. Density differences among the planets are chiefly a reflection of the nebular temperature at which the *dominant* accreting particulate matter equilibrated, as in the Equilibrium Condensation Model. Accretional energy heated the outer layers of the growing planets, as in the Reduction During Accretion Model. This melted the planets and allowed gravitational segregation of cores, mantles, and crusts; but the metallic iron for cores was probably not produced by in situ reduction, because nebular temperatures where the terrestrial planets accreted were probably too high to permit the condensation of carbonaceous compounds. Therefore, the planetary material did not contain the carbon needed to reduce oxidized iron (reaction (7-1)). Instead, the metallic iron came from metal grains like those found in ordinary chondrites (Fig. 5-7), which were formed in the nebula and accreted along with the other mineral components.

Finally, Heterogeneous Accretion supplied a veneer of low-temperature material to all the planets in the last stages of accretion. This was probably similar to Cl carbonaceous chondrites, and was condensed and accreted into planetesimals not in the region of the four terrestrial planets, but in the asteroid belt or even farther out in the solar system. During the $\sim 10^8$-yr phase of planetary assembly described earlier, in which planetesimals following eccentric orbits were swept up, the last to be swept would be those in the asteroid belt, farthest from the terrestrial planets. (Indeed, a great many such objects remain unswept to the present day!) Thus this type of low-temperature material would be added last to the accreting planets. From it came the atmospheres of Venus, Earth, and Mars; and it enhanced the degree of oxidation and the levels of volatile elements in the crust and upper mantle of our planet.

EARLIEST INTERNAL EVOLUTION OF THE PLANETS

The pattern of internal rearrangement followed by planets after they formed (perhaps even while they were forming) was crucially dependent upon the generation of heat and the rise of temperatures in them. The first small planetesimals formed in the solar system may have been heated by short-lived radionuclides such as ^{26}Al or by electric currents induced in them by the outward movement of plasma during the sun's T Tauri stage of evolution, but these heat sources probably would no longer be effective by the time the final accretion of the terrestrial planets was accomplished (Fig. 7-10).

As noted above, a major source of early heating in the terrestrial planets may have been the act of accretion itself. Each accreting planetesimal impacts at a velocity equal to or greater than the escape velocity of the forming planet. Virtually all the kinetic energy represented by this impact velocity is ultimately transformed into heat. When a growing planet is still small, its escape velocity is small (Eq. (2-4)), the energy of impact may be small, and the temperature rise may be modest. As the planet grows larger, however, it attracts planetesimals at higher and higher velocities, larger amounts of kinetic energy are converted to thermal energy, and a newly accreted planet may be hotter in its outer layers than at its center (see Fig. 7-12 and the initial temperature profile assumed in Fig. 4-7).

The temperature rise caused by accretion can be very large if all the heat generated by the process is retained: 1,300°K for the moon, 4,100°K for Mercury, 5,900°K for Mars, 25,000°K for Venus, and 29,000°K for Earth, averaged over the substance of each planet. However, it is not known how much of this

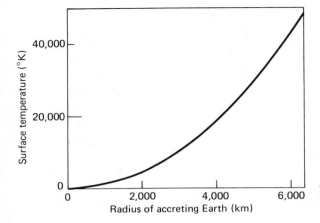

FIG. 7-12 Temperature rise of material joining a growing Earth as a function of the planet's size. This figure assumes that matter arrives at the escape velocity and the energy of impact is entirely converted to heat, which is conserved.

heat was actually retained by the accreting planets. If it was generated at the surfaces of the planets, most of the heat would have been radiated off to space during the protracted accretion of the latter. Collisions of major planetesimals with the growing planets, on the other hand, would have deposited some heat deep within them, where it could not readily escape.

Another source of early heat, especially for Earth and Venus, would have been core formation. If the dense substance of Earth's core was initially evenly distributed throughout the planet and began to trickle toward the center of the planet once melting started to mobilize the material of the Earth, this downward rain of heavy droplets would itself generate additional heat. The complete separation of Earth's core in this way would cause an additional temperature rise in Earth of $\sim 2,300°K$, on average.

Whatever the heating mechanism, the planets are generally believed to have been hot (at least partially molten, in fact) when they formed, largely because of the evidence in lunar samples of early melting and differentiation in the moon. Cores, mantles, and primitive crusts probably separated at this time, or soon after. A major portion of the atmospheres of the larger planets may have been outgassed at this time.

Subsequent evolution would have been keyed to the cooling of the outer layers of the planets and a thickening of their cool rigid lithospheres. As a lithosphere thickens and thermal activity retreats deeper and deeper in its planet, a point is reached where mantle convection can no longer break the lithosphere and move the fragments (plate tectonics), and internally generated basalt lavas can no longer erupt to the surface. One can, in fact, define a "life cycle" for planets (Fig. 7-13), and postulate that all planets followed it, but at different rates dependent mostly on their sizes.

In this scheme, the moon, which is small and loses heat readily, has evolved farthest along the track, to the point of senility in fact; it has not displayed volcanism for 3×10^9 yr, and if lunar plate tectonism was ever effective, it ceased prior to 4×10^9 yr ago, and all its surface effects were erased by the intense bombardment of planetesimals that scoured the moon and planets up to that time. Earth, on the other hand, has been able to husband its heat because of its large size, and is still in the full flower of volcanic and tectonic activity. The radical differences in surface morphology of the planets reflect this variability of the rate of evolution. Intense bombardment and cratering occurred only in the first 0.6×10^3 yr of solar-system history; Earth, which is still in a very active stage of geologic evolution, has obliterated all but the most recently inflicted of its craters. Mercury and the moon, where geologic activity abated before the intense bombardment did, still retain densely cratered surfaces.

The idea of planetary "life cycles" is a useful unifying concept, but it is important to remember that the evolutionary paths of planets are affected by more than just their cooling rates:

1. Compositions may differ. For example, Earth contains much more water than the moon. It has been pointed out that if Earth's upper mantle contained as little water as lunar rocks, it would be much more rigid than it is—too rigid to permit plate tectonic movements, in fact.

2. Differences in the sizes of planets affect not only their cooling rates, but also the pressure gradients in them. Pressures control the melting temperatures and stable mineral assemblages inside a planet.

3. Accretional energy can easily have melted the entire Earth at the outset, but could only partly melt the moon. If these things happened, Earth would subsequently cool throughout its volume, whereas the moon would cool on the outside but warm in its interior (as a result of radioactive element decay).

4. A planet large enough to hold an atmosphere experiences erosive processes and geochemical differentiation at its surface that an airless small planet does not.

FIG. 7-13 A first-order explanation for differences in the present geologic state of the planets, based on the proposition that cooling of the outer layers of planets brings on different stages of geologic activity (right edge of diagram), and small planets cool faster than large ones.

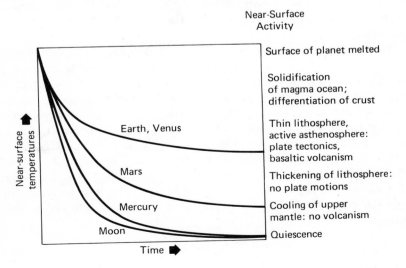

ORIGIN OF THE JOVIAN PLANETS

The preceding discussion has pertained only to the innermost four rocky planets. Something qualitatively different must have occurred in the outer reaches of the primordial nebula to give rise to the huge, low-density Jovian planets. As in the case of the terrestrial planets, two basically different modes of origin must be considered.

One is that the outer as well as the inner gaseous nebula was gravitationally unstable, and broke up into gas–dust fragments or protoplanets, as mentioned earlier. As the mass of the sun increased (as a result of the continuing addition of gas and dust from the nebula and from the outer reaches of the original interstellar cloud fragment), it would have exerted increasingly powerful tidal stresses on the protoplanets circling it, eventually tearing these gas concentrations apart and redispersing them in the nebula. If a portion of the dust component of each protoplanet had had time to settle to its center and form a dense core, however, before the gas envelope was dispersed, this solid core would not have been vulnerable to tidal disruption. Perhaps, as already noted, aggregations of this type joined together to form the terrestrial planets.

The disruptive effect of the growing sun would have been most strongly felt by the innermost protoplanets; as the solar mass, M, increased, its radius of destruction (the Roche limit, d) would have grown as indicated by Eq. (4-2). Perhaps tidal disruption was never totally effective beyond the mean distance of the asteroids. Some protoplanets in the outer nebula were able to retain part or all of their gases; these coalesced to form the present Jovian planets. Perhaps because the outer protoplanets had a longer time than the inner protoplanets before they began to feel strong tidal stresses, they had evolved (as described below) into sufficiently dense objects that ρ in Eq. (4-2) was able to offset M.

It is necessary to invoke partial dissipation of the protoplanets in the portion of the nebula where Uranus and Neptune were formed, however, and the dissipation had to be selective to remove the most volatile and abundant gases, H_2 and He, while leaving behind the icy and earthy components that these planets appear to be composed of. The details of this process have not been specified.

The other possible mode of origin is accretion at large in the nebula. As noted, it is expected that the nebula was warmest close to the protosun, and colder at greater distances. Lower temperatures permit the condensation of additional solids (Fig. 7-4); in this model, temperatures were low enough in the region of the Jovian planets to permit the condensation (or the survival, if they were never vaporized) of ices of H_2O, NH_3, and CH_4. The presence of this icey component is believed to have increased the efficiency of planetary accretion enormously, not so much because the ices were four times more abundant than earthy minerals in the nebula, as because "snowflakes" are expected to have a much greater tendency to adhere on contact, clump, settle to the midplane of the nebula, and coagulate to form planetesimals, than would earthy mineral grains.

It has been suggested that masses of ice and dust grew swiftly in the outer nebula (although it is unclear why they should have been spared the long period of gravitational perturbations, eccentric orbits, and destructive collisions that has been specified for the terrestrial planets). When some critical core mass was attained—probably 10 to 50 times the mass of Earth—a Jovian planet became gravitationally powerful enough to attract and hold uncondensed gases from the nebula. Evidently, accretion was most efficient at the inner edge of the region of the Jovian planets, where condensed material was most abundant; Jupiter and Saturn grew fastest and largest, exceeded the critical core mass, and captured huge amounts of nebular gases. This would account for the near-solar compositions of the models that describe them best (Table 4-4). Uranus and Neptune did not grow large enough to capture nebular gases, or if they did it was too late; the nebula had been dissipated.

Evolution of the Jovian Planets

A massive gas-rich planet like Jupiter or Saturn, once formed, would have gone through a process of gravitational contraction and internal heating (Helmholtz–Kelvin contraction) analogous to that followed by stars, as discussed in Chapter 6. At the outset, Jupiter would have been far larger than its present dimension, probably even larger than the present sun; and it would have been hot and luminous, emitting energy at about 1 percent the rate of the present sun.

Contraction would have caused its internal temperature to rise for the first $\sim 10^5$ yr, but then the point was reached where forces of electrostatic repulsion between the close-packed ions of metallic hydrogen in the deep interior of Jupiter began to support it against further contraction. Thereafter, heat was no longer generated by compression in the deep interior region, and the planet cooled. Presumably, Saturn followed a similar course. Jupiter's maximum internal temperature was never more than one tenth that needed to initiate nuclear fusion, which would have turned the planet into a main-sequence star. There is a critical stellar mass, about 7 percent that of the sun, above which Helmholtz–Kelvin contraction can lead to fusion reactions and "stardom"; objects smaller than this follow the path described for Jupiter.

In its present state, energy is being emitted from Jupiter's interior at only $\sim 10^{-9}$ the solar luminosity. Most of this is heat that was generated during Jupiter's early history of contraction, and its loss signals a cooling down of the planet; some is generated by additional contraction of the planets' outer, lower-density layers.

ORIGIN OF SATELLITES

Great uncertainty attaches to the origin of Earth's moon. Our satellite is unique in its large mass relative to that of the planet it circles; and we know now that its chemical composition is substantially different from that of Earth. Specifically, the low overall density of the moon shows it to be depleted in iron relative to Earth; and lunar samples have been found to be systematically depleted in the more volatile elements, compared with terrestrial rocks.

One hypothesis of lunar origin is fission from Earth: perhaps the latter spun so fast at the time when it was first formed that it threw off a chunk of its crust and mantle, which became the moon. If Earth's core had separated before this fission occurred, we might understand why the moon, derived from the outermost layers of Earth, is depleted in iron. This model has been criticized for requiring an improbably high planetary spin rate at the outset, and for producing an Earth–moon system with at least twice as much angular momentum as the present Earth–moon system.

Another possibility is that the growing Earth captured rocky rubble and dust from the nebula into orbit about itself, and the moon accreted from this disk of particulate matter. To capture approaching solid particles requires that they be decelerated as they pass Earth; in this model, deceleration is accomplished by collisions with other passing or orbiting particles. Approaching masses of metallic iron, being larger (less fragmented by previous collisions) and denser, would be less efficiently decelerated and captured, and incorporated less abundantly in the growing moon, than fragments of silicate minerals.

For either origin, the moon would have begun its existence in close Earth orbit, after which tidal interactions (Fig. 2-10) worked it out to its present distance. Material must have continued to be added to the moon during the $\sim 10^8$ years during which it appears that the terrestrial planets were being assembled. If it is true that a veneer of low-temperature volatile-rich material was added to Earth late in its accretional history, it is unclear why a similar layer was not also deposited on the moon.

The innermost satellites of Jupiter (Amalthea, Io, Europa, Ganymede, and Callisto), which move in orbits of very low eccentricity and inclination, may have been created in several possible ways. When Jupiter first formed and was distended and luminous, it may have been surrounded by a spun-out disk of gas and dust, a small-scale analogue of the primordial nebula in which it was embedded. The satellites named may have accreted from the Jupiter nebula in a manner comparable to the formation of the planets around the sun. Alternatively, they may have accreted from captured particulate matter in the absence of nebular gases, as suggested above for Earth's moon. The luminosity and warmth of proto-Jupiter would account for the relatively high density of the innermost of these satellites, which must consist largely or wholly of rock and contain little or no ice. Ganymede and Callisto, farther out, are less dense and are thought to contain a large component of water or ice.

The small, numbered outer satellites of Jupiter (Fig. 4-15), which move in more irregular (even retrograde) orbits, are believed to have been captured by the planet from heliocentric orbits.

These modes of origin are probably applicable to the satellites of the other Jovian planets, although many questions remain unanswered. The two small satellites of Mars, Phobos (Fig. 2-16) and Deimos, are also likely to be captured asteroids.

SOURCES OF ASTEROIDS AND COMETS

Asteroids are generally understood to be surviving planetesimals, or fragments thereof, from the earliest stages of accretion of the terrestrial planets. At the outset the total mass of asteroids in what is now the asteroid belt may have been very much larger than it is now, perhaps roughly equivalent to the mass of Mars. These object failed to merge into a single planet, as did the planetesimals closer to the sun; the gravitational influence of their next-outermost neighbor, massive Jupiter, is believed responsible for this. As Jupiter grew in size its gravitational field would have scattered the asteroid planetesimals more chaotically than any of the farther-in planetesimals. Consequently, impact velocities were higher among asteroids and encounters were more consistently destructive than was the case among the terrestrial planets. The asteroid planetesimals remained dispersed, became increasingly fragmented, and in time a large proportion of their mass was scattered to other parts of the solar system and swept up by planets, or was ejected from the solar system altogether.

Comets are also thought to be surviving planetesimals, except these accreted farther out in the nebula, beyond the position of Jupiter, where ices were stable and available for accretion, together with silicate dust. Again the orbits of these planetesimals were wildly perturbed by the gravitational fields of the outer Jovian planets as the latter grew. Many were thrown out of the solar system forever. Some were ejected at just slightly less than the escape velocity from the solar system, so that they coasted almost to a stop at the aphelia of extremely elongated elliptical orbits. It is this collection of not-quite-escaped planetesimals hovering about the sun at distances of tens of thousands of AU that comprises the reservoir of comets (Fig. 2-15) from which members occasionally swoop back down into the solar system.

Some of the cometary planetesimals were also thrown into the inner solar system, where they were soon destroyed by planetary impacts, mutual collisions, sublimation by the sun's heat, or ejection from the solar system. Cometary and asteroidal debris are thought to have been the source of the "low-temperature volatile-rich veneer" postulated above for Earth. Presumably, the other terrestrial planets were similarly coated.

PLANETARY SYSTEMS ABOUT OTHER STARS

The night sky is crowded with stars, and our romantic vision conjurs up systems of circling planets for most or all of them. Many of these planetary systems, we imagine, would include one specially favored planet where conditions of temperature, chemistry, and evolutionary history conspired to set the stage for the arisal of life, and where science-fiction-like civilizations now prosper.

In fact, relatively few of the stars in the galaxy can have planetary systems similar to our own. As noted earlier in this chapter, most stars in the galaxy are members of binary or multiple star systems; and it is difficult to find a stable orbit for a planet when it is subject to strong gravitational attractions by first one sun and then another. In these circumstances the planet would follow an irregular trajectory through the binary star system, as suggested in Fig. 2-7 for an asteroid in the sun–Earth system, until it collides with one of the suns or is ejected from the system. The regular progression of planets in near-circular orbits that characterizes our solar system would be impossible in a binary star system.

It would not be possible to see a planetary system about even the nearest star, using a telescope, because the planets (if present) would be so much dimmer and smaller than the star. Sometimes the presence of a large dark companion to a star can be inferred; since both objects orbit about their common center of mass, the trajectory of the luminous star through the galaxy is not a straight line, but has a very slightly wavy or corkscrewed character. There are many circumstances, however, in which the presence of a dark or even a luminous stellar companion is masked. The actual incidence of binary systems (i.e., stars accompanied by companions massive enough to disturb planetary systems; the critical mass ratio is probably about $\frac{1}{100}$ or greater) is extremely difficult to estimate; but it appears that at least 90 percent of the stars can be ruled out as hosts for solar-system analogues, and the proportion of effectively binary systems may be very much larger than that.

Actually, planets can exist in binary star systems (Fig. 7-14), but only in an orbital configuration unlike that of the solar system and not very conducive to

FIG. 7-14 Likely state of the solar system (not to scale) if Jupiter were 100 times more massive than it is, forming a binary star with the sun. The only stable orbits (solid lines) would be those that are very close to either of the stars (such as Mercury and the regular satellites of Jupiter) and dominated by their respective gravity fields, and those (e.g., Pluto) so far out from the binary pair that the gravitational attractions of the two stars seem to come from almost the same place. Other orbits, disturbed by the gravitational influence of two massive bodies that are continually changing position, would be unstable (dashed lines).

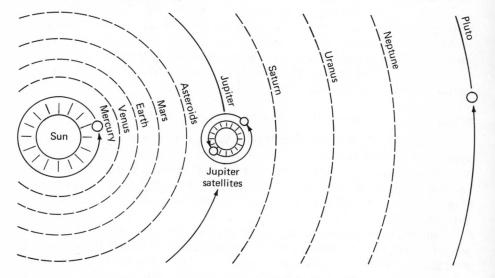

the arisal of life. In the example of Fig. 7-14, we know that Mercury would be far too hot and Pluto far too cold to permit the emergence of life. Life on a planet closely circling the smaller of the binary stars is an interesting thought, however; this star could be cool enough to maintain one of its close satellites/planets at a tolerable temperature. But such life-fostering planets would be possible only for secondary stars in a relatively narrow mass range: too small, and the "star" would never achieve internal nuclear fusion, instead cooling rapidly as Jupiter has; too large, and it would roast planets that were close enough to it to orbit stably.

In sum, although we have no reason to believe that Earth is the only repository of life in the galaxy, it does not appear likely that habitable planetary systems are abundant; and it seems quite possible that life, the vital enchantment that we so ingenuously take for granted, is an extremely rare phenomenon.

glossary of mineral names

The minerals mentioned in this book are briefly described below. No effort is made to provide a comprehensive survey of the mineral kingdom; the reader is referred to *Earth Materials* by W. G. Ernst (Prentice-Hall Foundations of Earth Science Series) for a more complete discussion of mineralogy.

anorthite *see* **plagioclase.**

chlorite soft, flaky, low-temperature mineral, $(Mg,Fe)_5Al_2Si_3O_{10}(OH)_8$, monoclinic, common in terrestrial metamorphic rocks.

chromite black oxide, $FeCr_2O_4$, cubic, minor constituent of terrestrial and lunar rocks and meteorites.

clinopyroxene *see* **pyroxene.**

cohenite opaque, bronze-colored, $(Fe,Ni,Co)_3C$, orthorhombic, minor constituent of iron meteorites.

corundum hard oxide, Al_2O_3, orthorhombic, minor constituent of some terrestrial metamorphic rocks. Sapphire and ruby are varieties of corundum.

diopside *see* **pyroxene.**

enstatite *see* **pyroxene.**

fassaite *see* **pyroxene.**

fayalite *see* **olivine.**

feldspar the class of minerals, very abundant in terrestrial and lunar rocks and meteorites, that includes **plagioclase** (which see) and orthoclase, $KAlSi_3O_8$.

forsterite *see* **olivine.**

garnet a family of minerals, cubic, having the general formula $(Ca,Mg,Fe^{2+},Mn)_3$ $(Al,Fe^{3+})_2(SiO_4)_3$; common in terrestrial metamorphic rocks. **Grossular** has a composition near $Ca_3Al_2(SiO_4)_3$; **pyrope** is near $Mg_3Al_2(SiO_4)_3$.

goethite oxide mineral, brownish, low-temperature, $Fe_2O_3 \cdot H_2O$, orthorhombic, common in terrestrial rocks.

grossular *see* **garnet.**

hisingerite low-temperature ferric silicate of uncertain composition, approximately $Fe_2O_3 \cdot 2SiO_2 \cdot nH_2O$, amorphous. Terrestrial, uncommon.

ilmenite black oxide, $FeTiO_3$, orthorhombic, ubiquitous constituent of terrestrial and lunar igneous rocks.

jadeite *see* **pyroxene.**

magnetite black oxide, Fe_3O_4, cubic. Common minor constituent of terrestrial igneous and metamorphic rocks; present in matrices of carbonaceous chondrites.

melilite a family of minerals ranging in composition between $Ca_2Al_2SiO_7$ and $Ca_2MgSi_2O_7$, tetragonal; present in some terrestrial metamorphic rocks, an important constituent of Ca,Al-rich inclusions in carbonaceous chondrites.

metal (nickel–iron) the pure metal alloys *kamacite* and *taenite*, both cubic, are major constituents of most meteorite classes.

montmorillinite soft, flaky, clay mineral, approximately $(Mg,Ca)O \cdot Al_2O_3 \cdot 5SiO_2 \cdot nH_2O$, monoclinic, present in terrestrial sediments and soils.

olivine an important family of minerals having the general composition $(Mg,Fe)_2$-SiO_4; orthorhombic. The magnesian end member is **forsterite**, the ferrous end member **fayalite**. Common in terrestrial and lunar igneous rocks; very abundant in meteorites; believed to be a principal constituent of planetary mantles.

orthopyroxene *see* **pyroxene**.

perovskite $CaTiO_3$, cubic, a minor mineral in terrestrial metamorphic rocks and the Ca,Al-rich inclusions of carbonaceous chondrites.

phyllosilicate the broad class of minerals with crystal structures that take the form of stacked sheets, which imparts a flaky or micaceous character to the mineral; includes **chlorite**, **montmorillinite**, various micas.

pigeonite *see* **pyroxene**.

plagioclase an important family of minerals ranging in composition between $NaAl$-Si_3O_8 (**albite**) and $CaAl_2Si_2O_8$ (**anorthite**); triclinic. Plagioclase composition is expressed as An_x, where x is the molecular percentage of the anorthite end member.

Abundant in terrestrial and lunar rocks; present in most meteorite classes.

pyrope *see* **garnet**.

pyroxene an important family of minerals, mostly describable by the formula $(Mg,Fe,Ca)SiO_3$. If Ca makes up less than 5 mole percent of the (Mg,Fe,Ca) group, the mineral is orthorhombic (**orthopyroxene**) in most cases. The most Mg-rich orthopyroxene $(Mg > 90$ percent) is **enstatite**. Pyroxenes containing more than ~ 5 percent Ca are monoclinic (**clinopyroxene**). Of these, **pigeonite** contains 5 to 15 percent Ca; **diopside** contains 45 to 50 percent Ca, and only 0 to 10 percent Fe. These pyroxenes are very common terrestrial, lunar, and meteoritic minerals.

Fassaite is an Al-rich clinopyroxene; **jadeite**, also monoclinic, has the formula $NaAl(SiO_3)_2$. Both are relatively rare in terrestrial rocks.

schreibersite grayish, opaque, tetragonal, $(Fe,Ni)_3P$. A minor mineral in iron meteorites.

serpentine a family of greenish, flaky, low-temperature minerals, common in terrestrial rocks, approximately $Mg_6Si_4O_{10}$-$(OH)_8$. Orthorhombic.

spinel a family of cubic oxide minerals having the general formula (Mg,Fe^{2+}) $(Al,Fe^{3+}Cr)_2O_4$. The spinel in Ca,Al-rich inclusions of carbonaceous chondrites is $MgAl_2O_4$. *Magnetite* and *chromite* are also spinels. A minor constituent of terrestrial and lunar rocks and meteorites.

troilite brassy, opaque, hexagonal, FeS. A major mineral in meteorites; a trace constituent in lunar rocks. (The equivalent terrestrial sulfide is pyrrhotite, approximately $Fe_{0.9}S$.)

suggestions for further reading

PLANETOLOGY

CHAPMAN, C. R., *The Inner Planets*. 170 pp. New York: Scribner's, 1977.

GOODY, R. M., and WALKER, J. C. G., *Atmospheres*. 150 pp. Englewood Cliffs, N.J.: Prentice-Hall, 1972.

HARTMANN, W. K., Cratering in the Solar System. *Scientific American*, vol. 236, no. 1, pp. 84–99, January 1977.

HARTMANN, W. K., *Moons and Planets: An Introduction to Planetary Science*. 404 pp. Belmont, Calif.: Wadsworth, 1972.

HEAD, J. W., WOOD, C. A., and MUTCH, T. A., Geological Evolution of the Terrestrial Planets. *American Scientist*, vol. 65, pp. 21–29, 1976.

KING, E. A., *Space Geology*. 349 pp. New York: Wiley, 1976.

LEWIS, J. S., The Chemistry of the Solar System. *Scientific American*, vol. 230, no. 3, pp. 51–65, March 1974.

SHORT, N. M., *Planetary Geology*. 361 pp. Englewood Cliffs, N.J.: Prentice-Hall, 1975.

The Solar System. 145 pp. San Francisco: W. H. Freeman, 1975. (This is a bound collection of the articles on the solar system that comprised the September 1975 issue of *Scientific American*: vol. 233, no. 3.)

EARTH

CLARK, S. P., Jr., *Structure of the Earth*. 132 pp. Englewood Cliffs, N.J.: Prentice-Hall, 1971.

HEEZEN, B. C., and MACGREGOR, I. D., The Evolution of the Pacific. *Scientific American*, vol. 229, no. 5, pp. 102–112, November 1973.

TOKSÖZ, M. N., The Subduction of the Lithosphere. *Scientific American*, vol. 233, no. 5, pp. 89–98, 1975.

WYLLIE, P. J., The Earth's Mantle. *Scientific American*, vol. 232, no. 3, pp. 50–63, March 1975.

THE MOON

FRENCH, B. M., *The Moon Book*. 287 pp. Baltimore, Md.: Penguin Books, 1977.

SCHULTZ, P., *Moon Morphology*. 626 pp. Austin, Tex.: University of Texas Press, 1976.

TAYLOR, S. R., *Lunar Science: a Post-Apollo View*. 372 pp. Elmsford N.Y.: Pergamon Press, 1975.

MARS

CARR, M. H., The Volcanoes of Mars. *Scientific American*, vol. 234, No. 1, pp. 33–43, January 1976.

LEOVY, C. B., The Atmosphere of Mars. *Scientific American*, vol. 237, no. 1, pp. 34–43, July 1977.

MUTCH, T. A. ARVIDSON, R., JONES, K., HEAD, J. W., and SAUNDERS, R. S., *Geology of Mars*. 400 pp. Princeton, N.J.: Princeton University Press, 1976.

Scientific Results of the Viking Project. Journal of Geophysical Research, vol. 82, no. 28, pp. 3959–4681, 1977.

COMETS AND ASTEROIDS

CHAPMAN, C. R., The Nature of Asteroids. *Scientific American*, vol. 232, no. 1, pp. 24–33, January 1975.

WHIPPLE, F. L., The Nature of Comets. *Scientific American*, vol. 230, no. 2, pp. 49–57, February 1974.

METEORITES

GROSSMAN, L., The Most Primitive Objects in the Solar System. *Scientific American*, vol. 232, no. 2, pp. 30–38, February 1975.

WASSON, J. T., *Meteorites.* 316 pp. New York: Springer-Verlag, 1974.

JOVIAN PLANETS

CRUIKSHANK, D. P., and MORRISON, D., The Galilean Satellites of Jupiter. *Scientific American,* vol. 234, no. 5, pp. 108–116, May 1976.

INGERSOLL, A. P., The Meteorology of Jupiter. *Scientific American,* vol. 234, no. 3, pp. 46–56, March 1976.

NEWBURN, R. L., Jr., and GULKIS, S., A Survey of the Outer Planets Jupiter, Saturn, Uranus, Neptune, Pluto, and Their Satellites. *Space Science Reviews,* vol. 3, pp. 179–271, 1973.

STARS AND GALAXIES

ABT, H. A., The Companions of Sunlike Stars. *Scientific American,* vol. 236, no. 4, pp. 96–104, April 1977.

AVRETT, E. H., ed., *Frontiers of Astrophysics.* 554 pp. Cambridge, Mass.: Harvard University Press, 1976.

BOK, B. J., The Birth of Stars. *Scientific American,* vol. 227, no. 2, pp. 49–61, August 1972.

PASACHOFF, J. M., *Astronomy Now.* 400 pp. Philadelphia: W. B. Saunders, 1978.

STROM, S. E., and STROM, K. M., The Early Evolution of Stars—I and II. *Sky and Telescope,* vol. 45, no. 5, pp. 279–282, May 1973, and no. 6, pp. 359–361, June 1973.

index